Young Readers Nature Library

THE SEA

Young Readers Nature Library
Adapted from the LIFE Nature Library

THE SEA

Leonard Engel
and the Editors of TIME-LIFE BOOKS

TIME-LIFE BOOKS, ALEXANDRIA, VIRGINIA

ON THE COVER: This black-tipped
shark, one of the five types named
for their distinctive black fin markings,
is approximately eight feet long. The
species is usually found off the Atlantic
and Gulf coasts of Florida.

Contents

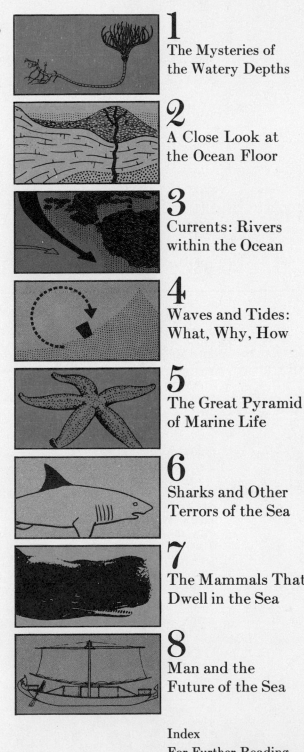

1

The Mysteries of the Watery Depths

Our planet has the wrong name. Our ancestors, who believed that the sea was only a narrow river surrounding the rocks and soil on which they lived, named this planet Earth, after the land they found all around them. If they had known what the earth was really like, they undoubtedly would have named it Ocean, after the tremendous areas of water that cover almost three fourths of its surface.

In the sun's family of planets the earth is unique in its possession of oceans. Indeed it is remarkable that oceans exist at all. They do only because the largest part of the earth has a surface temperature in the small range within which water remains a liquid: in short, between 32° F. (below which, under ordinary conditions, water freezes) and 212° F. (when it boils and becomes a gas).

In a surprising variety of ways, the prop-

GILDED BY LIGHT, a stretch of ocean reaches to the horizon and beyond. Though apparently deserted, these vast waters brim with countless living forms. Here dwell plants and animals so small they cannot be seen by the naked eye. Here also is the home of the blue whale, a giant that reaches 100 feet in length.

erties of liquid water seem almost to have been purposely designed to make the world a place where life can exist. Water has an unusually high capacity for storing heat, for example. As a result, the oceans act as great heat reservoirs that cool the earth in summer and warm it in winter.

Another important characteristic of water is that it can dissolve more substances than any other liquid known. No life could exist on earth for a moment if water did not have this capability. Living organisms, big and small, are chemical factories that carry on the business of life by means of an amazing variety of chemical reactions. Many of these reactions can take place only when water is present to dissolve the reacting substances and bring their molecules together. Furthermore, water forms part of many of the chemical compounds found in living tissue. Seventy per cent of the human body is water. All forms of life need water—which, even for plants and animals that live on land, must come ultimately from the oceans.

The oceans' unique importance to life is equaled by their great size. Together they

A Stubborn Survivor

Sea lilies, animals with flowerlike bodies, have been discovered in fossil form in rock that is more than 300 million years old *(left)*. Unlike other ancient marine creatures that are now extinct, sea lilies adapted to life in the sea so well that they still survive in a form *(right)* very little changed from their early ancestors.

cover 141 million square miles, more than 70 per cent of the entire surface of the earth. The largest of the four oceans is the Pacific (equal in size to the other three oceans combined): then come the Atlantic, the Indian, and the Arctic. With their fringing gulfs and smaller seas, they make up an interconnected system that forms a girdle stretching around the globe.

The oceans contain about 350 million cubic miles of water; the volume of all land above sea level is only one eighteenth as great. The tallest peak on land, the 29,028-foot-high Mount Everest, could be sunk without a trace in the greatest sea canyon, the 36,204-foot-deep Mariana Trench in the western Pacific. Locked up in all this water is a great variety of minerals in solution. Oxygen, carbon dioxide and nitrogen from the atmosphere are also found dissolved in sea water. Dissolved oxygen is what marine creatures breathe. Dissolved carbon dioxide is used by green plants in the sea to produce food. Dissolved nitrogen produces nitrates that nourish plants in the sea.

The most noticeable of the ocean's minerals are salts, chiefly sodium chloride—ordinary table salt, which is what makes sea water taste salty. Sea water is about 3.5 per cent salts; a cubic mile of sea water contains 166 million tons of the salts, and the sea as a whole contains enough to cover the continents with a layer 500 feet thick.

Where do all the salts in the sea come from? Some come from the breaking up of rocks by frost and erosion. This gradual wearing away of mountains has released minerals locked up in rock and allowed them to be dissolved by rain water and carried to the ocean. The rest of the salts has been soaked out of rocks under the ocean bed.

The minerals that have washed from the land into the ocean are only a tiny portion of the total material that eventually finds its way to the sea. The ocean is the earth's great catch basin. Sooner or later almost everything ends up there. Black mud that once grew corn and cotton in the Mississippi Valley, the debris resulting from the grinding down of a hundred mountain ranges, the

scourings from 10,000 river channels—all of these are on the ocean bottom. So are dust, volcanic ash and even tiny meteorite globules from outer space.

To this mixture is added the debris that the sea itself creates. When marine organisms die, their remains drift downward. A part of this unending "rain" never reaches the bottom because it is eaten on the way down by deeper-dwelling organisms or because it is dissolved by sea water and floats toward the surface. Over a long period of time, however, a great quantity of marine debris settles on the ocean floor.

In relatively shallow waters, where sea life is richest, and near the mouths of rivers, where debris from land is deposited, the accumulation of sediment can be as much as 30,000 to 40,000 feet thick. Even in the deepest parts of the ocean, sediment can be more than a mile thick.

Through most of his history man has been studying only the surface of the sea, as a source of food and as an avenue for travel.

Descendant of an Extinct Species

The horseshoe crab (above) is a sea animal that has remained almost unchanged over millions of years of evolution. On the other hand, a relative of the horseshoe, the giant trilobite (left), is now extinct. The fossil trilobite shown here, about 18 inches long, is one of the multitude that ruled the earth as sea-floor scavengers for about 100 million years.

Now, however, he is plumbing the ocean depths. Although man's knowledge of this vast, underwater world is still very incomplete, there has been more sounding and exploration of the ocean bottom since 1950 than in all the rest of history.

The depth record for a manned undersea exploration is held by the crew of the *Trieste*. This vessel, a type that is known as a bathyscaph, was designed to penetrate the depths of the ocean, and on January 23, 1960, the *Trieste* spent 20 minutes on the bottom of the sea, deep inside the Mariana Trench—nearly seven miles down. But most of man's present knowledge of the depths has not come from such record-breaking achievements. We are learning about the ocean in much the same manner that we have been learning about space—by inventing instruments and techniques that make it possible not only to explore many areas firsthand but also to obtain important information without the necessity of man's presence.

Already some astonishing discoveries have been made. One of the most unexpected is that there are significant geological differences between the land and ocean areas. Oceanographers, scientists who study the sea, now know that the land and sea are distinctly different. The continents are made of granitic rock; the bed of the deep ocean, however, consists of a heavier kind of rock called basalt. Another piece of surprising new knowledge is that the earth's crust—the thin outermost layer—is far thinner under the sea than it is on land. Equally extraordinary was the discovery of the Mid-Ocean Ridge, a 47,000-mile mountain chain under the sea that is by far the longest range in the world.

But not even this new knowledge of geology is as surprising as the startling and interesting variety of life in the sea. No one can make an accurate guess at the number of individual organisms that live there.

The life of the ocean is divided into distinct zones, each one with its own group of creatures that feed upon each other and depend on each other in different ways. There is, first of all, the tidal zone, where land and sea meet. Then comes the zone of the shallow seas around the continents, a region that extends down to about 600 feet. It is in these two zones that the vast majority of all marine life occurs.

The deep ocean adds two regions, the zone of dim light that extends to about 3,000 feet and the zone of perpetual darkness. When the *Trieste* descended into the clear waters of the western Pacific, for example, light could still be seen through its portholes at a depth of 1,000 feet. But for practical purposes the zone of light ends at about 600 feet. Below that, there is too little light to support the growth of the "grass" of the sea—the tiny, single-celled green plants whose ability to form sugar and starch with the aid of sunlight makes them the ultimate source of all things that live in the ocean.

The natural history of the sea and devel-

Land Bridges of the Past

The earth did not always look as it does today. At times, for example, continents now separated by water were joined by land bridges. Thus, animals and plants that first evolved in Asia could pass by land to North America and vice versa *(left, top)*. This land bridge has been exposed numerous times. It is believed that the first humans in North America came by this bridge. The European land bridges *(left, middle)* show how Britain was once linked to the continent and Spain and Italy were once joined to North Africa.

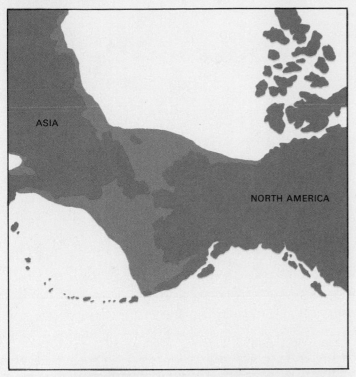

NORTH AMERICA AND ASIA

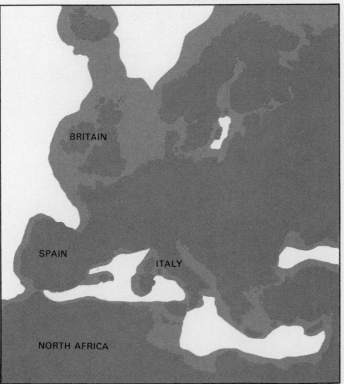

GREATER EUROPE

FORMER LAND BRIDGES

THE CONTINENTS TODAY

opment, or evolution, of the plants and animals that live there are really the story of life itself. For all animals—including man—and all plants that now live on the land descend from organisms that once lived in the sea.

The sea is old, old almost beyond imagining. And the earth itself is still older. Most scientists believe that the earth was born some five billion years ago but that the sea did not begin to fill with water until some time later. Some scientists believe the water came from rocks as the earth cooled. It may have reached the atmosphere in the form of vapor and collected into clouds. As the temperature of the earth continued to drop, the vapor condensed and fell as rain.

Most scientists believe that life on earth may have appeared as early as 3.5 billion years ago. This estimate is based in part on bacteria and algae fossils found in South Africa in rocks that are known to be at least 3.1 billion years old.

The assumption of modern science is that the first "living" things were tiny organisms possessing the ability to reproduce themselves—the property that more than anything else distinguishes living things from nonliving. Simple, and single-celled, these microorganisms must have first taken shape in the sea, because water was necessary to their formation.

Then a second event happened, which was almost as important as the leap into life itself. Certain living organisms acquired the ability to capture energy from sunlight and

14

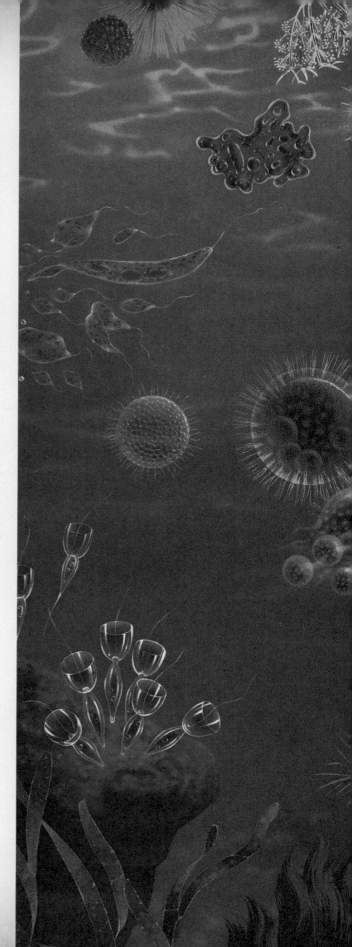

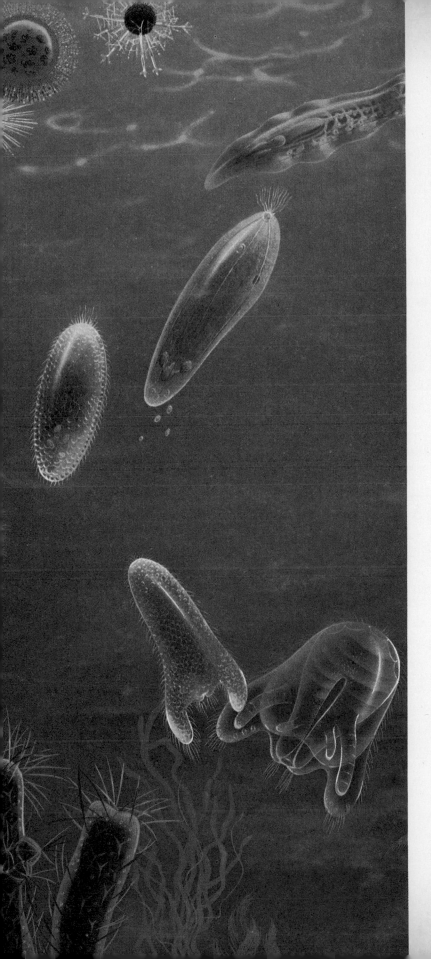

The Basis of All Life

Blobs of protoplasm—simple plants and
animals belonging to the protista kingdom
—float in the sea. These tiny objects are
believed to be modern descendants of one
of the first forms in which life appeared.
Protistans are eaten by slightly larger
creatures, which in turn are consumed by
still larger sea dwellers and so on up the
ladder. Thus, these protistans are among
the basic building blocks of life in the sea.

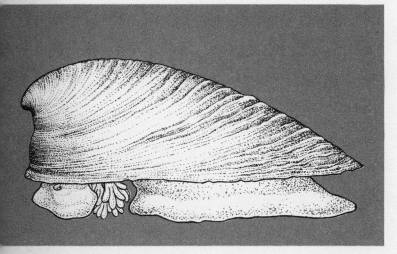

use this energy to make food out of the chemicals that had been dissolved in the ocean. These living things took the carbon dioxide that is dissolved in sea water and, by using sunlight, were able to produce sugar, at the same time releasing oxygen.

The ability to perform these complicated acts was not acquired all at once, but over a long period and in several stages. The organisms that continued to use this process were plants. Other organisms, unable to perform this miracle (called photosynthesis) but still needing organic food, found that they could live on plants. These were animals.

From the day that life first awoke in the waters, the sea has been a cradle endlessly rocking. Among the earliest organisms that can be traced to the ocean are the blue-green

Holdovers from Ancient Days

Two sea creatures that have survived almost unchanged from their earliest beginnings are the mollusk called *Neopilina (above)* and an odd-looking fish named coelacanth *(right)*. *Neopilina* was thought to have been extinct for 350 million years. However, in 1952 living specimens of the one-inch animal were discovered in an ocean trench some two miles deep. The coelacanth was also believed extinct, but in 1938 live specimens were netted off South Africa. This fish is the world's oldest living higher animal; it probably developed about 300 million years ago. The fish is covered with blue scales and its lobed fins are attached to the body by stalks.

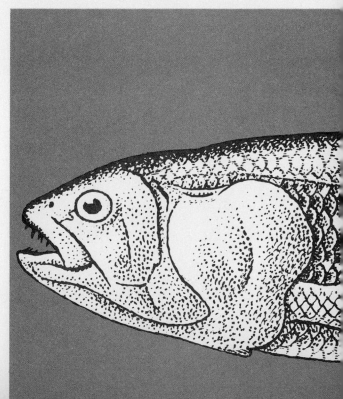

algae and rod-shaped bacteria. They are still prevalent today. Yet, curiously, plants never evolved to any high degree in the sea. Today, there are fewer than a hundred species of "higher" plants flourishing in ocean waters—compared with some 250,000 flowering plants on land. The story of water-dwelling animals, on the other hand, is quite different. Almost from the time that the jump was made from single-celled to many-celled forms, animals began to display an amazing variety of shapes.

The record of fossils imprinted in rock is our source for the early history of living things. Until a few years ago, such records began with what scientists called the Cambrian period, whose rocks were formed 600 to 500 million years ago. That period was marked by the first appearance of animals with the hard shells that make good fossils. The creatures that preceded them had such soft bodies that they left behind comparatively few traces of themselves.

Recently, however, at least 130 million years of history were added with the discovery, in England and Australia, of many impressions left in ancient, hardened mud by Precambrian animals. Through these records we know that some 700 million or more years ago, there were jellyfish (the most primitive creatures with a mouth and stomach), as well as segmented worms and creatures like flatworms (among the first organisms with a nervous system and brain).

(Text continued on page 22)

1 MANTA 20 FT.
2 BLUE MARLIN 10 FT.
3 SAILFISH 8 FT.
4 FLYING FISH 9 IN.
5 SUNFISH 7 FT.
6 OCEANIC BONITO 2 FT.
7 DOLPHIN 4 FT.
8 PILOT FISH 9 IN.
9 WHITE-TIPPED SHARK 7 FT.
10 BLUEFIN TUNA 7 FT.
11 GIANT SQUID 55 FT.
12 SPERM WHALE 60 FT.
13 STERNOPTYX DIAPHANA 2 IN.
14 DIRETMUS ARGENTEUS 2 IN.
15 EEL LARVA 4 IN.
16 HATCHET FISH 1 IN.
17 LAMPROTOXUS FLAGELLIBARBA 8 IN.
18 PLATYBERIX OPALESCENS 3 IN.
19 ROOSTERFISH 15 FT.
20 VIPERFISH 12 IN.
21 PRAWN 4 IN.
22 PHOTOSTOMIAS GUERNEI 7 IN.
23 LANTERN FISH 3 IN.
24 CHIASMODON NIGER 2 IN.
25 OPISTHOPROCTUS SOLEATUS 1 IN.
26 MELANOCETUS JOHNSONI 2 IN.
27 SNIPE EEL 2 FT.

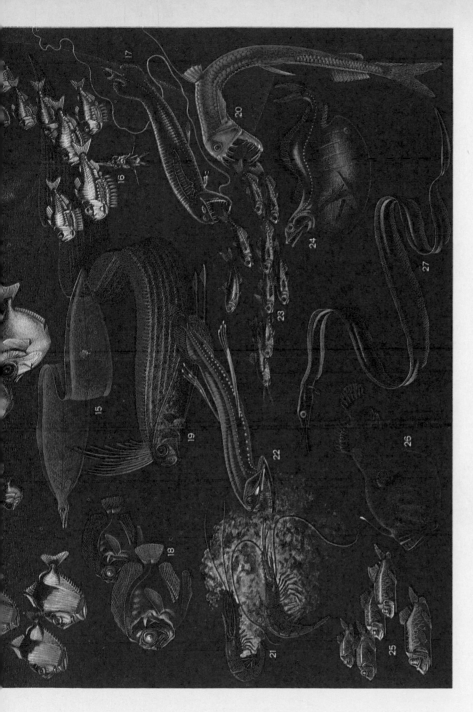

The Fish and Mammals That Rule the Sea

Animals with backbones rule the sea. They differ from all other animals by having a rigid support —the backbone—inside the body. In some primitive sea animals such as the shark the backbone is little more than a tough rod wrapped in elastic tissue. In most fish, however, the backbone is a flexible cord of bones called vertebrae, to which powerful muscles are attached. It is the backbone and the muscles, controlled by a complex nervous system, that have made the aquatic animals the masters of the sea.

The painting above shows fish and mammals that live in a 4,000-foot-deep cross section of the sea; the painting key lists the creatures and their average lengths. Familiar food and sport fish race in the upper waters and burst through the surface. Here too swim the sharks, the 3,000 pound manta ray and a huge ocean sunfish that dwarfs a man. In the mid-depths, a backboned whale, the world's largest animal, battles with a giant squid, the largest animal without a backbone. Farther down live creatures known only by their scientific names. One tiny dweller of the deep, the Chiasmodon niger, can swallow prey larger than itself. In the lowest levels only body patterns of glowing color identify friend from foe.

19

1 SEA COLANDER	17 SUN STAR	32 BAY SCALLOP SHELL
2 SEAWEED	18 MOON SNAIL SHELL	33 JINGLE SHELLS
3 MUSSEL SHELL	19 BOAT SHELL	34 GREEN CRAB
4 EDIBLE MUSSELS	20 DOG WHELKS	35 HERMIT CRAB
5 PINK-HEARTED HYDROIDS	21 PERIWINKLES	36 SOFT CORAL
6 REDBEARD SPONGE	22 PURPLE SEA STAR	37 SEA CUCUMBER
7 RIBBED MUSSELS	23 CORALLINE ALGAE	38 PURPLE SEA URCHIN
8 COMMON SEA STAR	24 BLOOD SEA STAR	39 WHELK EGG CASE
9 RAZOR CLAM SHELL	25 SAND DOLLAR AND SHELL	40 SKATE EGG CAPSULE
10 OYSTER DRILLS	26 MUD STAR	41 LADY CRAB
11 ROCK BARNACLES	27 BRITTLE STAR	42 BLUE CRAB
12 IRISH MOSS	28 ROCKWEED	43 TORTOISE-SHELL
13 SEA GRAPES	29 ROCK CRAB	LIMPETS
14 SEA VASES	30 GREEN SEA URCHIN AND	44 SEA SPONGE
15 SEA ANEMONE	SHELL	45 EYED-FINGER SPONGE
16 SEA PORK	31 SEA PEACHES	46 YOUNG HORSESHOE CRAB

The Teeming Life of the Shore Bottom

The painting above shows a few square feet of shallow ocean bottom along the New England coast of the United States. Here sea animals flourish, taking from the splashing water life-giving oxygen and the dissolved minerals that they require to make shells and bones. But there is also danger. Predators, attracted by the abundance of prey, cruise in search of easy meals. Waves and tides tear at the unanchored animal and toss it ashore to die.

Evolution has given the animals that live on the coastal bottoms the equipment to survive these onslaughts. Shallow-water sponges have fingerlike bodies that offer less resistance to the surging waters than do the bodies of the vase-shaped sponges that live in the deeps. The sea stars, or starfish, creep along the bottom at six inches a minute and hold on to the rocks with such a strong grip that their suction-cup feet will part from their bodies before they will let go.

The wealth of fossils from the Cambrian time that followed offers a much fuller picture of early life. There were no animals possessing backbones and no plant or animal had evolved that was capable of moving out of the sea and onto the land. The sea, especially the sunlit shallows, remained the nursery of life. Animals with protective shells, plates and skins multiplied there. Lamp shells, snails and graptolites (drifting creatures with fantastic branching skeletons) appeared. But the most important forms were the arthropods, something like today's crabs and lobsters. The chief of the arthropods of the Cambrian sea floor was a many-legged creature called the trilobite.

In the Ordovician period that followed (500 to 440 million years ago), the arthropods gave way to giant mollusks called nautiloids, whose shells were up to 16 feet long. Sea stars and corals put in their appearance. It was not until the Silurian age (440 to 400 million years ago) that fish—the first animals with backbones—arrived on the scene in abundance. The other great event of the Silurian period was the invasion of the land by the higher plants. This occurred after the emergence of great mountains had the effect of driving the sea back and uncovering low-lying land areas. Soon afterward two small animals, the sea scorpion and the spider, crawled up on the beach and stayed.

By the next era, the Devonian (400 to 350 million years ago), many fish had multiplied into forms that can be recognized as strangely familiar relatives of modern fish. The vastly increased mobility, adaptability and strength of these fish had made them the dominant form of marine life. A few of them followed the scorpion ashore and developed into the first land-dwelling vertebrates (animals with backbones). Man is descended from such fish that left the sea.

It was in the periods after the Devonian that life really began to evolve on the land. Of course, it would continue to develop in the sea as well; new types of fish and other forms of marine life replaced older ones. And the boundaries of the sea would change as great sheets of ice spread down from the poles, shifting the borders between land and ocean. But the main drama of life had already moved to a new domain—the land.

The Fiery Birth of an Island

Belching acrid, sulphurous smoke, a volcano erupts from the sea near Japan and creates a new island. This particular island was formed in 1952; other islands have been born elsewhere since then. As volcanoes erupt, their fumes often stain neighboring waters for days and kill great numbers of fish.

2

A Close Look at the Ocean Floor

AN UNDERWATER LANDSLIDE takes place on the ocean floor off the coast of Lower California. Such landslides occur when masses of sand, dumped into the sea by streams and rivers, pile up on the edge of an underwater cliff. Finally, the weight becomes too great and the sand sweeps down the slope.

In the days when great sailing ships first set off across the oceans, man's ideas about the sea were mostly based on myths or wrong information. For one thing, people believed that the ocean floor was more or less flat. Now we know that nothing could be further from the truth. The same varied features seen on land—huge mountains, plunging canyons, broad plateaus, narrow valleys, steep cliffs—are all found on the ocean bottom. In fact, the ocean floor is, if anything, *more* rugged than land, because there is far less erosion on the ocean floor than there is on land.

The ocean floor stretching away from a land mass is divided into at least three great domains. First, there is the continental shelf, a shallow border zone crammed with life. Then come the continental slopes, where the undersea extension of a continent ends. Finally, there is the deep ocean basin.

The shelves skirt almost all of the earth's coasts, reaching outward for an average of about 48 miles from the shoreline and gradually carrying the land down to a depth of about 500 feet. Parts of the shelves were above the waterline during the Ice Age, when a tremendous amount of water was locked up in glaciers, thus lowering the amount of water in the oceans. For example, discoveries of mammoth teeth many miles off the shore of continents indicate that now-submerged land was once dry.

At the outermost edge of the continental shelves, the ocean floor slopes downward for two or three miles. In most places, the slopes are fairly gentle. But where mountains crowd a coast and there is little shelf, the descent can be more than five miles from the top of a mountain to the bottom of an adjacent trench. This happens along the coast of Chile where the Andes reach the seashore.

At the foot of the slope, there is often a more pronounced slant that marks the edge of a continental portion of the earth's crust; this slant is aptly called the continental rise. In some places, as at various spots on the Pacific side of the Americas, there are deep trenches instead of a continental rise. Trenches also occur in the plain of the deep ocean, beyond the continental slope. The deep ocean basin is the biggest undersea zone, being five sevenths of the total sea area.

The one device that has been most helpful in mapping the ocean floor is an instrument called a continuous recording echo sounder. An echo sounder sends a beep of sound down into the water and then measures how long it takes for the echo to return to the surface; the length of time between the sending of the sound signal and the detection of an echo indicates how deep that floor lies. An early version of such a device was developed in 1911 by Reginald Fessenden, a United States engineer. It was a great advance from the old practice of dropping a long, weighted hemp line or a piano wire from a ship (to measure depth this way, the ship had to spend hours in one place). The echo system devised by Fessenden allowed the ship to keep moving, but it was both an imprecise and tedious process. The sound wave was of low frequency, which made it spread out in the water and cover a broader area than a directional, high-frequency wave would do. Furthermore, the reading was given in time, which then had to be converted to depth and recorded by hand. Subsequently, it was plotted on a chart.

A way to record continuous soundings

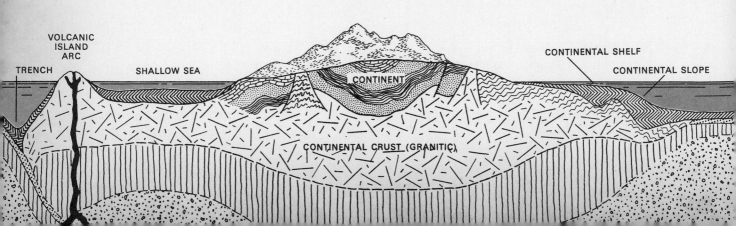

VOLCANIC
ISLAND
ARC

TRENCH   SHALLOW SEA   CONTINENT   CONTINENTAL SHELF
                                                                  CONTINENTAL SLOPE

CONTINENTAL CRUST (GRANITIC)

was developed in the 1930s, but soundings were at first limited to depths less than 6,000 feet. Only after the Second World War, when scientists developed more sensitive echo-detecting instruments, was it possible to take soundings of the deepest parts of the ocean, where the most startling discoveries have been made. These discoveries are of such magnitude that the period in which we live can certainly be considered the second great era of discovery, rivaling the 15th and 16th centuries, when much of the earth's surface was explored.

The most important result of the new age of exploration is the theory of plate tectonics. This theory explains how the upper layer of the earth—the lithosphere—is divided into a dozen or so sections, called plates. The rigid plates are in slow but constant motion, moving over a hot, soft layer called the asthenosphere—and causing both the continents and the undersea terrain to slowly move about in the process.

Much of our knowledge about the movements of these plates comes from studies of an extraordinary undersea formation called the Mid-Atlantic Ridge. The existence of

Ups and Downs of the Sea Bed

Typical land and sea forms are portrayed in this cross section of the earth's upper layers. The main ingredient of the continent is granitic rock, which is lighter but bulkier than the basalt of the ocean bottom. As a result, the continent stands high above the oceans. At the left, one crustal plate dips down under another, creating a trench and an island arc. At the right, melted material from the asthenosphere oozes up through the Mid-Ocean Rift to form new ocean floor.

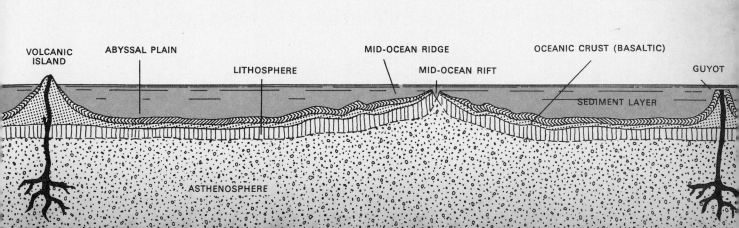

VOLCANIC ISLAND   ABYSSAL PLAIN   MID-OCEAN RIDGE   OCEANIC CRUST (BASALTIC)

LITHOSPHERE   MID-OCEAN RIFT   GUYOT

SEDIMENT LAYER

ASTHENOSPHERE

the ridge has been known for some time. Hints of its presence had accumulated since 1873, when a rise in the middle of the Atlantic Ocean was discovered by the old depth-measuring technique of using weighted lines. Then in the 1930s and 1940s oceanographers used the continuous echo-sounding system along this rise and decided that the ridge is really a rugged underwater mountain chain.

In 1953, Bruce G. Heezen and some of his colleagues at the Lamont Doherty Geological Observatory in New York found that a rift—a steep-sided valley—runs down the center of the chain. Furthermore, he discovered that earthquakes, which were known to occur in the Mid-Atlantic Ridge, were centered precisely at the rift. Heezen, along with Lamont's director, Maurice Ewing, began plotting the locations of earthquakes in the floors of other oceans. Records indicated that quakes occur along a continuous line running for almost 50,000 miles as it curves around the world in a pattern roughly resembling the seams of a baseball.

In 1956, the two scientists bravely predicted that this enormously long quake line would mark the location of a continuous mid-ocean ridge. Subsequent echo soundings have proved them right. And when scientists also learned that abnormally high temperatures are present along this long ridge, it became clear that mid-ocean formations are special places indeed.

A few scientists began to think that the ridges are sites where lithosphere plates are

(Text continued on page 38)

PORTRAITS OF THE OCEAN BED

A Look at the World with the Oceans Removed

The maps of the Arctic and Antarctica on the opposite page and those on the following eight pages were prepared by cartographer Kenneth Fagg to show another world—the world as it would look with all the water drained away. Land areas are depicted in silvery white. Although the maps cannot show all the details of the ocean floors, the variety and ruggedness of the features are easy to see.

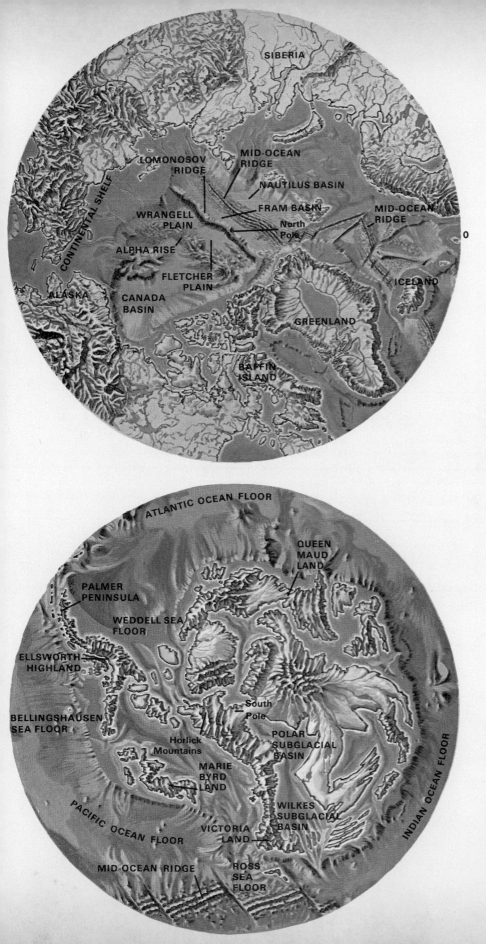

THE DEEP BASINS in the center of the Arctic Ocean lie at great depths beneath the thick ice crust. The deepest of all is the Fram Basin, more than 3,000 miles below sea level. It runs from Greenland to the broad, shallow continental shelf of Asia.

THE ANTARCTIC is a continent largely covered by ice. It is surrounded by the Atlantic, Pacific and Indian Oceans and by its own small seas. A 2,263-mile-deep trough slices through the continent to join the Weddell and Ross Seas together.

Coiling like a giant snake, the Mid-Atlantic Ridge—
part of the vast undersea Mid-Ocean Ridge—is
featured in this view of the Atlantic Ocean north
of the equator. The continents of Africa and Europe
are at the right, the Americas at the far left. The
ridge, which bisects the Atlantic, varies in width
from 300 to 1,200 miles and takes up a third of
the ocean floor. It is split down the center by a deep
rift that runs along its entire length. The ridge
surfaces at a few places, creating Iceland, the

THE NORTH ATLANTIC

GREENLAND
ICELAND
GIBBS FRACTURE ZONE
FLEMISH CAP
NEWFOUNDLAND
MILNE SEAMOUNT
ANTIALTAIR SEAMOUNTS
GRAND BANKS
LAURENTIAN CHANNEL
ALTAIR SEAMOUNTS
MID-OCEAN CANYON
HUDSON CANYON
SOHM ABYSSAL PLAIN
Azores Islands
KELVIN SEAMOUNTS
OCEANOGRAPHER FRACTURE ZONE
CORNER SEAMOUNTS
Madeira Islands
HATTERAS CANYON
MUIR SEAMOUNT
CRUISER GUYOT
GREAT METEOR SEAMOUNT
Canary Islands
BERMUDA RISE
ATLANTIS FRACTURE ZONE
FLORIDA
BLAKE ESCARPMENT
HATTERAS ABYSSAL PLAIN
RIFT MOUNTAINS
CAPE VERDE ABYSSAL PLAIN
VEMA GAP
KANE FRACTURE ZONE
PUERTO RICO TRENCH
MID-ATLANTIC RIDGE
Cape Verde Islands
CONTINENTAL RISE
COLOMBIA ABYSSAL PLAIN
BEATA RIDGE
AVES RIDGE
CONTINENTAL SLOPE
DEMERARA ABYSSAL PLAIN
VENEZUELA
VEMA FRACTURE ZONE
ST. PAUL FRACTURE ZONE
St. Paul Rocks
CEARA ABYSSAL PLAIN
BRAZIL
Equator

75W   60W   45W   30W

Azores and the St. Paul Rocks. At right angles
to the ridge are crevasses called fracture zones; the
sides of the ridge were formed by molten rock that
rose through the rift and later cooled. Earthquakes
occur along the rift's valley and in the fracture
zones. The abyssal plains, some two to three miles
below sea level, are the deepest parts of the North
Atlantic except for the four-mile-deep Puerto Rico
Trench. To the north are many guyots (undersea
volcanoes) and seamounts (submerged mountains).

Fernando
de Noronha
Island

ROMANCHE
FRACTURE ZONE

CHAIN FRACTURE ZONE

PERNAMBUCO
ABYSSAL
PLAIN

BRAZIL

MID-ATLANTIC RIDGE

CONTINENTAL RISE

TRINIDAD SEAMOUNT LINE

VAZ ABYSSAL PLAIN

RIO GRANDE PLATEAU

MID-ATLANTIC RIDGE

ARGENTINE ABYSSAL PLAIN

ARGENTINE RISE

Falkland
(Malvinas)
Islands

FALKLAND ESCARPMENT

SANDWICH
TRENCH

South Georgia
Island

South Orkney
Islands

South Sandwich Islands

THE SOUTH ATLANTIC

The Mid-Atlantic Ridge also exists in the South
Atlantic and is the most prominent feature of this
part of the undersea world. Curving to the east
past the 25,748-foot deep Romanche Trench, the
ridge pokes above water at a few places, creating
islands like St. Helena and Ascension, and broadens
as it continues southward. The smaller Walvis
Ridge branches off toward Africa. Knifing down the
Mid-Atlantic Ridge's back is the same rift found in
the north. It winds around Africa in the Atlantic-

32

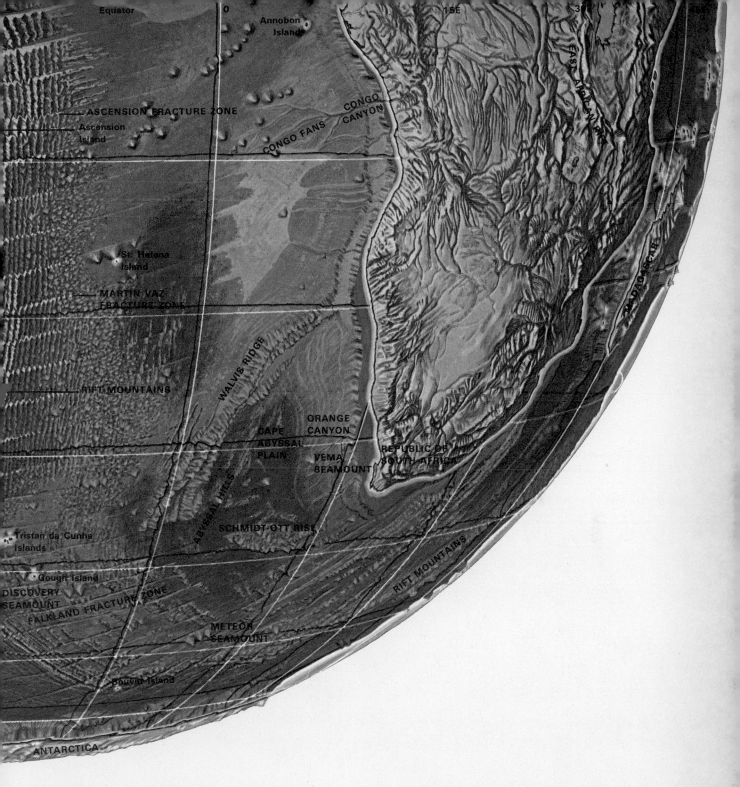

Annobon
Island

ASCENSION FRACTURE ZONE

Ascension
Island

CONGO FANS

CONGO CANYON

EAST AFRICAN

St. Helena
Island

MARTIN VAZ
FRACTURE ZONE

WALVIS RIDGE

MADAGASCAR

RIFT MOUNTAINS

ORANGE
CANYON

CAPE
ABYSSAL
PLAIN

VEMA
SEAMOUNT

REPUBLIC OF
SOUTH AFRICA

ABYSSAL HILLS

SCHMIDT-OTT RISE

Tristan da Cunha
Islands

RIFT MOUNTAINS

Gough Island

DISCOVERY
SEAMOUNT

FALKLAND FRACTURE ZONE

METEOR
SEAMOUNT

Bouvet Island

ANTARCTICA

Indian Ridge, and a splinter runs up the Red Sea.
The abyssal plains flanking the ridge are the resting
place for silt from land. Sometimes the sediment
rolls down the continental shelf in avalanches, and
possibly helps carve underwater canyons like the
Congo Canyon. In some places the continental shelf
juts far offshore, then drops in sheer cliffs. To the
south, the Sandwich Trench is the deepest part of the
South Atlantic—extending more than five miles
below sea level.

The Pacific Ocean, whose northern half is shown below, is the largest single feature of the earth's surface, bigger than all the continents together. It also contains the earth's greatest heights and depths. The Mariana Trench (*below, far left*) is a gaping hole more than six miles deep. Toward the center of the Pacific's great bowl, the volcanic cones of the Hawaiian Islands poke up as much as 32,000 feet above the sea floor (higher than the 29,028 feet Mount Everest rises above sea level). An important

THE NORTH PACIFIC

feature of the Pacific bottom is the East Pacific Rise, part of the Mid-Ocean Ridge that parallels the coasts of Central and South America. This ridge extends into the North American continent by way of the Gulf of California and the San Andreas Fault.

Several gigantic fracture zones, running east and west, split the Pacific. The largest of these fractures in the ocean floor are the Mendocino, Murray, Clarion and Clipperton zones. In some places these are 30 miles wide and more than two miles deep.

HODGKINS RIDGE

PATHFINDER SEAMOUNT

PLAIN

NE

GREAT TROUGH

COBB BANK

ONEER DGE

MENDOCINO RIDGE

DELGADA FAN

SAN ANDREAS FAULT

MOONLESS MOUNTAINS

ERBEN GUYOT

MONTEREY FAN

RACTURE ZONE

FIEBERLING GUYOT

Guadalupe Island

JASPER SEAMOUNT

GULF OF CALIFORNIA

RACTURE ZONE

HENDERSON SEAMOUNT

Revilla Gigedo Islands

CUBA

CAYMAN TROUGH

LARION FRACTURE ZONE

CALIFORNIA SEAMOUNT

MIDDLE AMERICA TRENCH

MATHEMATICIANS SEAMOUNTS

TEHUANTEPEC RIDGE

CLIPPERTON RIDGE

GUATEMALA BASIN

CLIPPERTON FRACTURE ZONE

EAST PACIFIC RISE

COCOS RIDGE

GALAPAGOS FRACTURE ZONE

Equator

135 W

120 W

105 W

Galápagos

90 W

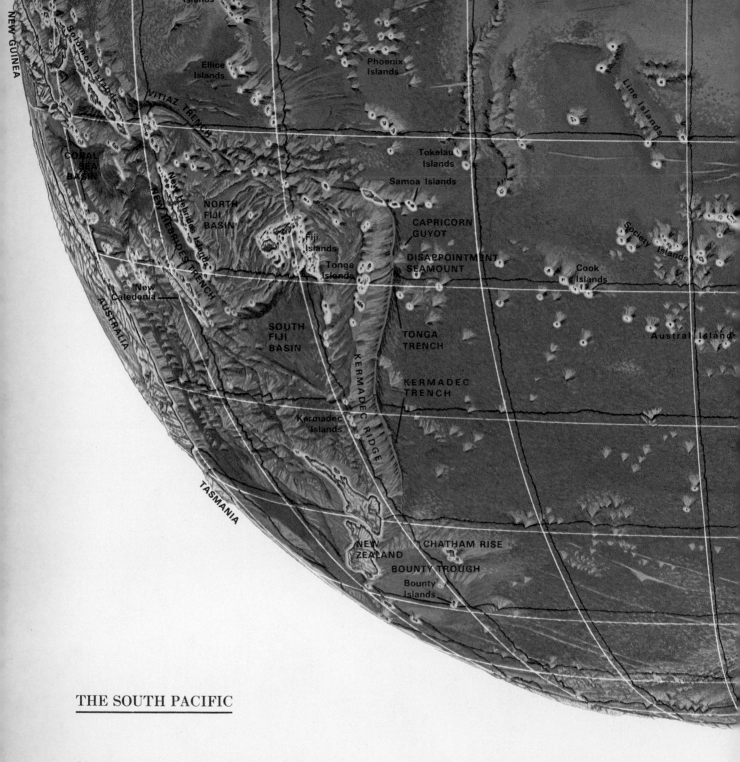

THE SOUTH PACIFIC

One of the most impressive features of the Pacific Ocean is the Tonga-Kermadec Trench on the left. It is a crease in the ocean floor that is almost seven miles deep and about 1,600 miles in length—big enough to hold half a dozen Grand Canyons. The rest of the ocean floor is dotted with seamounts and domed hills 100 to 3,000 feet high; their tops lie two to three miles below sea level. Hundreds of tiny coral atolls, however, manage to rise above sea level. Scientists have found that the amount of heat

36

GALAPAGOS
FRACTURE ZONE

Islands

CARNEGIE
RIDGE

Marquesas
Islands

EAST PACIFIC RISE

PERU

MARQUESAS   FRACTURE   ZONE

BAGEL
SEAMOUNT

HELEN
SEAMOUNT

NASCA RIDGE

Tuamotu
Archipelago

PERU-CHILE
TRENCH

San Félix
Island

EASTER   FRACTURE   ZONE

Pitcairn
Island

Easter
Island

CHILE

Juan Fernández
Islands

GIFFORD
SEAMOUNT

SOUTH
CHILE
RIDGE

PACIFIC-ANTARCTIC RIDGE

ANTARCTICA

flowing from the ocean bottom at certain spots can
be six times greater than normal for the ocean floor.
One such spot, the Galápagos Fracture Zone, is
really another rift where new sea floor is created and
near which eruptions of very hot, mineral-laden

water occur. Scientists have coined their own names
for some Pacific features they discovered: one
undersea peak along the Tonga Trench was called
Disappointment Seamount because some dredging
tools were lost there.

37

being forced apart because of upwelling of molten volcanic material from the earth's interior. Melted rock is called magma while it is still below the surface. When it erupts or oozes up at the surface, it is called lava. According to the scientists, lava emerging at the mid-ocean rifts cools and solidifies to become new lithosphere.

This theory raised a difficult question: if new sea floor is being created at the rifts, why isn't the earth expanding? Obviously, old lithosphere is disappearing even as new lithosphere emerges—but where does the disappearance take place? Figuring out the answer was the last step in the development of the theory of plate tectonics. Deep trenches, which—like the undersea mountain range—are marked by earthquakes and volcanic activity, seemed logical spots where lithosphere could be consumed. This would happen if two moving plates met in such a way that one slid under the other and was pulled into the asthenosphere. Cores of ocean-bottom sediment taken by research ships added some supporting evidence for this idea. The cores showed that while the lithosphere was new at mid-ocean rifts and bridges, it was old—150 million years old—at the trenches.

But scientists could not be sure the new theory was correct until they took a first-hand look at one of the spots where new sea floor was supposedly coming into existence. The place they chose for this crucial investigation was the Mid-Atlantic Rift.

Luckily, the basic technology for first-hand deep-sea exploration was available. As far back as the 1930s, a thick-walled, ball-shaped container known as a bathysphere had carried the American naturalist William Beebe to oceanic depths. The bathysphere's buoyancy could not be controlled, however, and the device therefore had to be lowered and raised on a cable dangling from a ship on the surface. Then, a Swiss explorer, Auguste Piccard, developed an undersea craft called a bathyscaph, which carried lead shot for ballast and tanks of gas for buoyancy; these improvements permitted the craft to move about on its own, free of a supporting cable. During the 1960s scientists of various nationalities designed a large number of other submersibles, as the free-moving undersea vessels were called. They carried from two to six men, and they were equipped with cameras, coring devices to sample the crust, mechanical arms to gather rock, water samplers, nets to catch deep-sea creatures, and powerful lights.

To inspect the Mid-Atlantic Rift, the submersibles would have to dive 7,800 to 9,800 feet. This would be undersea adventure that was like no other in history. It was like an expedition to the moon.

French and U.S. scientists planned the project, having already had considerable experience with research submersibles. However, British and Canadian scientists were also involved. The program was correctly called the French-American Mid-Ocean Undersea Study, but most people knew of it simply as Project FAMOUS.

When the project got under way in 1971, both France and the United States had a submersible more or less ready to use in the project, but there were problems. The French craft, a bathyscaph named *Archimède*, could go even deeper than required, but it was large and difficult to maneuver. The smaller U.S. submersible, the *Alvin*, whose interior has been compared to the inside of a fine Swiss watch, could not dive beyond 5,900 feet. Consequently, in 1972 the *Alvin* was fitted with a new titanium pressure hull that would protect it against pressure on dives all the way down to 11,800 feet. At the same time, the French set about preparing another craft in addition to the *Archimède*. Called *Cyana*, it was much like the *Alvin* in its size and maneuverability. But the *Cyana* was flatter and less angular, and as a result it was called a "diving saucer."

The place that was selected for exploration was a 60-square-mile area located southwest of the Azores Islands, west of Gibraltar. This general area was already well known from many years of surveys by research ships. Surveys that were made specifically for Project FAMOUS began in the autumn of 1971 when magnetic patterns of the region were recorded from the air. Then for a period of two years, ships crossed and crisscrossed the area, using echo sounders in order to create maps of the undersea terrain. Automatic cameras were dropped to the bottom and took the first photographs of the region —thus revealing oddly shaped lava forms. Earthquake instruments recorded the con-

tinual occurrence of small quakes that were taking place in the rift.

Toward the end of the preparation for diving, an eight-foot-long instrument package called a "fish" was towed by the United States research ship *Knorr* to obtain still finer detail of the rift valley. It could take photographs, record sediment thickness and detect the magnetic makeup of underlying rock. Still other instruments were used for more soundings, more readings and more photographs.

In the summer of 1973, the *Archimède*, escorted from the Azores by its mother ship, made seven dress-rehearsal dives into the rift's inner valley, which was only one mile wide. The main purpose of these preliminary dives was to find out what working conditions would be like for the three craft, especially the bulky *Archimède*, when the major exploration began the following year. The very first dive placed the *Archimède* next to a wall of rock about 300 feet high, where a bottom current proved to be far swifter than had been anticipated. In fact, the current was strong enough to make the submersible somewhat difficult to control, and the hull scraped against rocks several times. A subsequent check on currents was reassuring. Most of them were caused by tides and none of them would be hazardous.

By the time the seven dives were completed, the *Archimède* had proved that it was quite possible to move about in the rugged terrain, not only to collect samples but also to take photographs and gather data for careful mapping and documentation. Then, in June 1974, the *Alvin* and the *Cyana*, along with their mother ships, joined the *Archimède* for the culmination of the most elaborate deep-sea project ever attempted.

It took up to an hour for the submersibles to reach their 8,800-foot-deep destination. Scientists aboard the vessels saw huge formations of lava everywhere. This left no doubt that molten rock from the earth's interior is indeed rising at the rift, creating new sea floor as the plates of the earth's lithosphere move in opposite directions.

Even though some of the lava masses had already been spotted in photographs, the explorers gathered a great deal of new and important information about this amazing valley at the center of the deep-sea mountain range. One interesting formation of lava that had not shown up well in photographs was a cone-shaped pile made up of balls of lava that had poured out from an opening in the rift. These piles had not been well detected before because they had the same composition and color as other rocks resting on the sea floor. Such a pile received the name of "haystack."

The explorers were especially fascinated by another type of solidified lava outflow, which they called a "toothpaste formation." These masses of relatively new lava dribbled down the side of hills and out of bumps on the inner valley floor. The inner valley as a whole turned out to be a dramatically creviced region, with cracks that stretched from the central line of the valley to the outer walls. The widest cracks, located the farthest distance from the center, were between 30 and 330 feet deep. In addition, jagged fractures cut across the rift. It would seem that sea-floor spreading is truly an earth-wrenching process.

In one of the fracture zones, the French team found deposits of manganese oxide—a mineral that is a valuable source of copper, nickel and cobalt. How did it get there?

It seems likely that, at least at some spots of a rift, sea water mixes with mineral-rich magma. Then the heated water rises, carrying with it a burden of dissolved minerals. As the water cools down once again, these minerals solidify, and are deposited on the ocean floor.

No matter how the manganese oxide arrived in the Mid-Atlantic Rift, its presence puts an entirely different aspect on deep-sea exploration. We are becoming increasingly aware that minerals—including lead, zinc, gold and silver, in addition to those that can be extracted from manganese oxide—abound on the ocean floor, and Project FAMOUS shed further light on areas where they can be found. Already a great deal of interest has been aroused by the possibility that we can actually mine what lies at the ocean bottom. Many plans are under way, and large-scale mining operations—using suction devices or huge scoops—may begin in the near future. The sea floor, mankind's newest frontier, may well turn out to be a major source of raw material for tomorrow's world.

Traveling into the Deep

The two craft below are answers to a serious
problem faced by underwater explorers: the pressure
of deep water. On land, an average force of 15
pounds presses on every square inch of a man's body.
Under water, the forces increase tremendously.
The problem is to build craft sturdy enough to
withstand the pressure, but maneuverable enough
to perform useful work. The *Alvin* is designed to work
at depths up to 12,000 feet, where the pressure is
two and a half metric tons per square inch. It has air-
filled spheres near the rear for buoyancy and a
mechanical arm in front for probing. The *Archimède*,
which is able to descend almost seven miles, uses a
tank filled with gasoline for buoyancy and metal
pellets to make it sink. When the pellets are
released, the *Archimède* rises to the surface.

ALVIN

ARCHIMEDE

41

Plate 5

A
CHART
of The
GULF STREAM

James Poupard, *sculp.*

3
Currents: Rivers within the Ocean

The sea's waters are always moving. If you dive into the surf, some of the water particles that cling to your back may have just arrived after years of travel from an ocean 10,000 miles away. The surface waters move up in whirlpools, half an ocean in size. The deep waters—always cold no matter what the surface temperature—flow at mystifying speeds, some slow, some fast. Even individual currents move more rapidly at some points in their journey than at others.

This restlessness is almost as much a part of the sea as its wetness. The best way to understand its constant motion is to take a long-range view of the earth turning through space, spinning on its axis in such a way that the seas near the equator receive the sun's direct rays. Thus they get much more heat than do the polar seas. That fact alone would be enough to set the oceans stirring. When

THIS GULF STREAM CHART was drawn in 1770 for Benjamin Franklin to show the course of the mighty current. Franklin had gotten the information from American seamen who rode eastward with the flow to save two or more weeks on a crossing. Eventually all sailors adopted the time-saving route.

Forces That Shape Currents

Three factors affecting the speed and direction of ocean currents are illustrated in the drawings below. In the tropics, the sun's rays strike directly, concentrating a lot of heat in a small area instead of spreading it out, as happens near the poles. As tropic seas warm up, they expand and flow "downhill" toward the poles. The second factor, the earth's rotation, spins the currents in the Northern Hemisphere to the right and those of the Southern Hemisphere to the left. This is the Coriolis effect. These two factors—uneven sunlight and the spinning, or Coriolis effect—combine to produce global wind belts. These winds blow out of the northeast and southwest in the Northern Hemisphere, and out of the southeast and northwest in the Southern Hemisphere. All three factors produce clockwise surface currents in the Northern Hemisphere and counterclockwise ones in the Southern.

the sun warms the surface water at the equator, the water expands, and the sea level here actually tends to be a few inches higher. This is not much, but it produces a tiny slope. As a result, this surface water pushes "downhill" toward the North and South Poles. On the other hand, far to the north and south of the equator the heavier cold water (heavier because water contracts as it cools) sinks below the warm and spreads along the bottom toward the equator, though in a circuitous route.

The interchange of warm equatorial and cold polar waters is one of the most important of the sea's movements. But it is complicated by the sweep of other great forces also set in motion by the earth's whirling.

As the earth spins on its axis it creates a force that works to speed up water along the western shores of the oceans. Nor is that all, for the spin also causes the water to veer

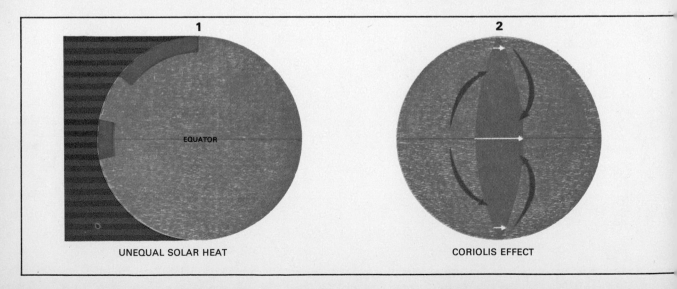

1

EQUATOR

UNEQUAL SOLAR HEAT

2

CORIOLIS EFFECT

slightly to the right in the northern half of the world, toward the left in the southern. This is called the "Coriolis effect," after the Frenchman who first described it.

Another equally important force that produces movement of the waters is the wind —also set in motion by the rotation of the earth. The steadiest winds on earth are those at the edge of the tropics, the trade winds. These blow westward toward the equator in both hemispheres, then wheel northeast and southeast to help drive the currents in both the Northern and the Southern Hemispheres along their great curving routes.

One of the first men to engage in the scientific study of ocean currents and proclaim their importance to mankind was Benjamin Franklin. He noted that American ships commonly took about two weeks less to cross the Atlantic than English vessels. When Franklin asked a cousin, a whaling captain from Nantucket Island, about this difference, he learned that American captains heading for Europe were taking advantage of a current running eastward across the North Atlantic at three miles an hour; on their way home Yankee seamen were piloting their vessels so as to avoid this mighty eastward-flowing current as best they could.

Using this information, Franklin had a chart drawn showing the course of the great river in the sea *(pages 42-43)*. At the bottom of the chart, he inscribed the words "Gulf Stream." Franklin's chart, drawn for the use of all ships sailing across the Atlantic (the haughty British skippers ignored it for the first few years), was the first systematic chart of an ocean current ever published.

The Gulf Stream remains a fascinating current to study. We look upon it today as part of a single great ring, or gyre, as oceanographers call it, extending over the whole North Atlantic basin. As its name suggests,

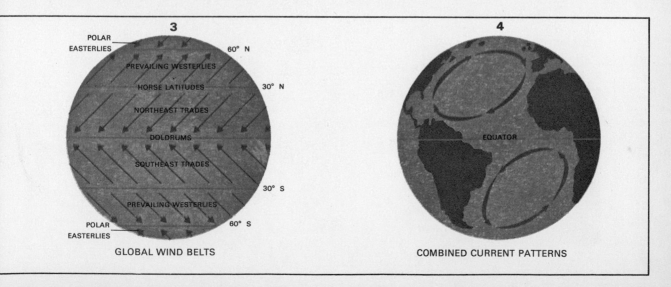

3

POLAR EASTERLIES — 60° N

PREVAILING WESTERLIES

HORSE LATITUDES — 30° N

NORTHEAST TRADES

DOLDRUMS

SOUTHEAST TRADES

PREVAILING WESTERLIES — 30° S

POLAR EASTERLIES — 60° S

GLOBAL WIND BELTS

4

EQUATOR

COMBINED CURRENT PATTERNS

this huge current is born in the Gulf of Mexico. It reaches the Atlantic Ocean through the Straits of Florida and, under numerous names, moves in a great clockwise circle off the coasts of North America, Western Europe and northwestern Africa before completing the circle near the West Indies.

In the middle of the ever-turning circle of North Atlantic currents is the fairly still region known as the Sargasso Sea. This may be thought of as the hub of the North Atlantic wheel—a very large hub, about 1,000 miles wide and 2,000 miles long. Moreover, like most wheel hubs, it sticks out of the plane of the wheel; scientists have found that the water level of the Sargasso Sea is as much as four feet higher than that along the Atlantic Coast of the United States. This "bump" is the result of a variety of causes, one of them being the expansion of the almost still Sargasso waters by the sun's rays.

In the South Atlantic, the North and South

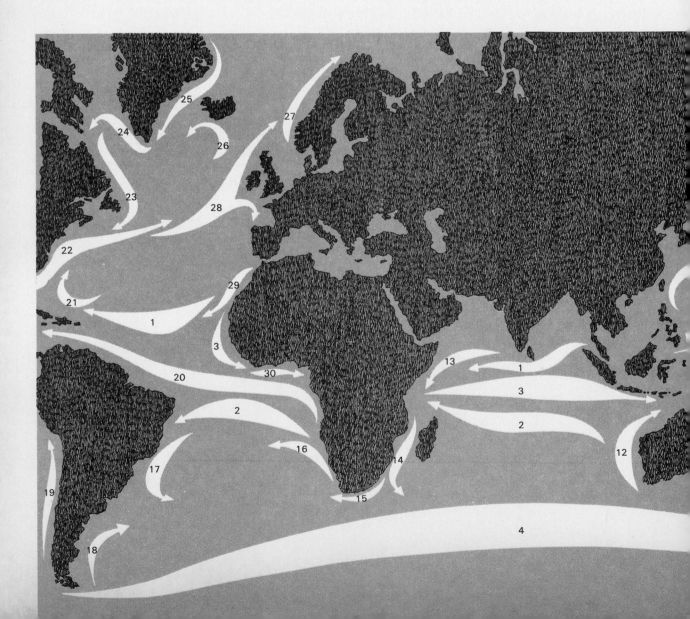

Pacific, and the Indian Oceans, there are similar turning wheels, though not all the circling currents are as strong as in the North Atlantic system. The current wheels of the South Atlantic almost duplicate those in the North, but in the reverse direction; because southern currents are on the other side of the equator, they run counterclockwise.

The northwestern Pacific has its counterpart of the Gulf Stream in the Kuroshio Current. Skirting Taiwan and the Japanese islands, this strong current warms Canada and Alaska and delivers the same nourishing rain showers to the coasts of British Columbia, Washington and Oregon that the Gulf Stream, at this stage of its journey called the North Atlantic Current, bestows upon the coasts of northwestern Europe.

These, and similar drifts of the Indian Ocean, are the main surface currents that keep water circulating in the large oceans. But they only begin to illustrate the com-

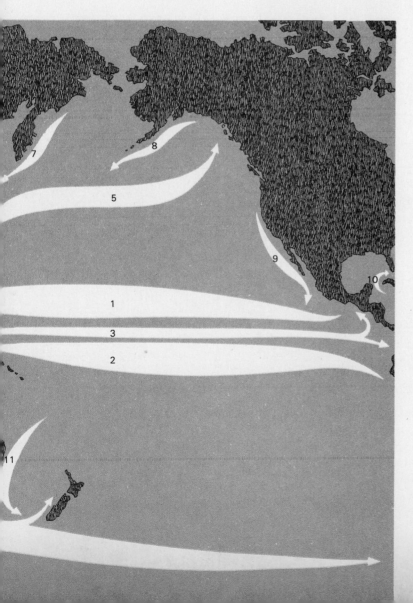

Trails across the Sea

Currents—mighty rivers of moving water—move through all the world's seas. Thirty of the major ocean currents are mapped at left. Long-term currents, which flow all year long, are pushed along by differences in the weight of water. These differences arise from varying water temperatures and salt content. The currents are shaped by the earth's rotation and prevailing winds and curve when they near land masses. In the days before sail, currents transported migrating people on rafts—a feat duplicated by scientists who floated with the South Equatorial Current across the Pacific on a small craft of balsa.

1. NORTH EQUATORIAL CURRENT	16. BENGUELA CURRENT
2. SOUTH EQUATORIAL CURRENT	17. BRAZIL CURRENT
3. EQUATORIAL COUNTERCURRENT	18. FALKLAND CURRENT
4. ANTARCTIC CIRCUMPOLAR CURRENT	19. PERU CURRENT
5. NORTH PACIFIC CURRENT	20. GUIANA CURRENT
6. KUROSHIO CURRENT	21. ANTILLES CURRENT
7. OYASHIO CURRENT	22. GULF STREAM
8. ALEUTIAN CURRENT	23. LABRADOR CURRENT
9. CALIFORNIA CURRENT	24. WEST GREENLAND CURRENT
10. FLORIDA CURRENT	25. EAST GREENLAND CURRENT
11. EAST AUSTRALIAN CURRENT	26. IRMINGER CURRENT
12. WEST AUSTRALIAN CURRENT	27. NORWEGIAN CURRENT
13. SOMALI CURRENT	28. NORTH ATLANTIC CURRENT
14. MOZAMBIQUE CURRENT	29. CANARY CURRENT
15. AGULHAS CURRENT	30. GUINEA CURRENT

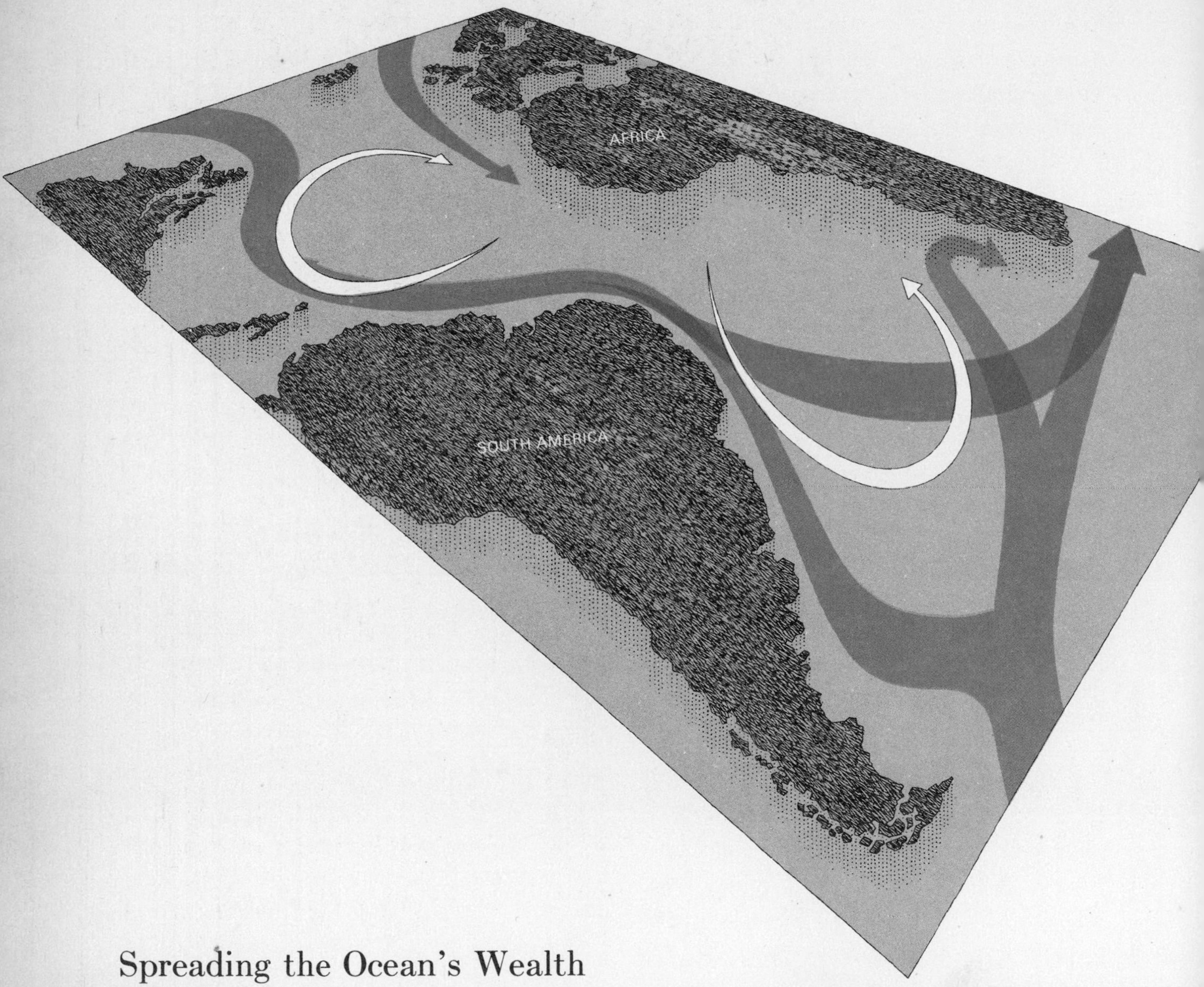

Spreading the Ocean's Wealth

Major currents vital to life in the Atlantic Ocean are mapped above. Deep currents run far below the surface currents (*white*), which extend downward usually 3,000 to 5,000 feet. These cold, oxygen- and mineral-rich waters from the poles flow toward the equator at depths below 10,000 feet. When the deep water surfaces—a phenomenon known as upwelling —it is often along coastlines. Where upwelling occurs, plankton, a basic food for fish, thrives; this in turn leads to a large fish population.

SURFACE CURRENTS

ANTARCTIC DEEP CURRENT

ARCTIC DEEP CURRENT

48

plex—and often unexplained—total movement of ocean water. Most of our knowledge of currents goes back little more than a century, when a United States Navy lieutenant, Matthew Fontaine Maury, published the first worldwide wind and current charts.

In the 1870s, a British team of scientists, headed by Sir Charles Wyville Thomson, spent three and a half years studying the ocean aboard the first ship ever equipped for sea exploration, H.M.S. *Challenger*. The results of this exhaustive effort launched the science of oceanography. Since World War II, when many technological advances were made, oceanographers have developed ever-more-precise ways to learn about all parts of the ocean—including the currents that flow at great depths, often under other currents.

One current like this was discovered almost by accident by the United States Fish and Wildlife Service. A research vessel of the service was in the central Pacific in 1951, testing a Japanese tuna-fishing technique known as long-line fishing, which involves trailing cables several miles long to which are attached smaller fishing lines that dangle downward. To the scientists' surprise, this gear began drifting to the east instead of the west. A year later, Townsend Cromwell of the Fish and Wildlife staff made further investigations and traced the drift to a huge and previously unknown current that flows eastward, about 300 feet beneath the west-flowing South Equatorial Current. This submarine current, only 600 feet thick, turned

out to extend at least 3,500 miles, travel almost as fast as the Gulf Stream and carry nearly half the Gulf Stream's load of water. It is called the Cromwell Current in honor of its discoverer.

On the heels of the discovery of the Cromwell Current came another, this time in the Atlantic. During the work of the International Geophysical Year in 1957 and 1958 (a cooperative effort by scientists of 66 nations to study both outer and "inner" space), a joint British-American expedition located a sizable current below the Gulf Stream. It was detected at depths of 6,600 to 9,800 feet and was flowing in the opposite direction from the Gulf Stream.

We have already seen that cold water is heavier than warm and tends to sink. Salt, too, makes water heavy. Near melting glaciers, however, the water tends to be less salty because the ice that is melting is nearly fresh. By contrast, the water near ice that is beginning to form will have more than an average amount of salt since the ice that is in the process of freezing leaves extra salt behind in the water. Since this kind of water—both cold and salty—will sink the deepest, the heaviest water is found at the very bottom of the sea.

There are also regions of the sea with strong up-and-down movements. Probably the most interesting interchange of rising and sinking streams of water occurs in the Antarctic Circumpolar Current, which is believed to be the largest current of all. Uninterrupted by continents as it flows around Antarctica, it swings northward because of the earth's rotation and westerly winds. Actually the current is composed of two layers, not just one. The upper one is cooled by melting surface ice of glaciers. The other layer is the Antarctic Bottom Water, which apparently is the coldest water in the world.

As the cold current moves northward, it is replaced by the relatively warmer waters of the Atlantic, Pacific and Indian Oceans. When the opposite-flowing currents meet, the icy surface current, even though it is less salty, sinks beneath the warmer water and continues northward as an intermediate layer in the ocean. An even more curious thing happens to the Antarctic Bottom Water in the Atlantic after it has crept all the way to the West Indies. Here it meets another cold current, called the North Atlantic Deepwater (*page 48*), flowing southward. Though the North Atlantic water is saltier, the Antarctic Bottom Water is so cold that it remains true to its name and flows beneath the North Atlantic water.

Cold water can also rise from considerable depths to fill a space when surface water is carried away. Such movements are called upwellings. They are vital to the life of the sea and to man; they bring minerals with great nutritional value to the upper layers of the sea, where most marine life dwells. The world's most important fisheries are to be found in areas of upwelling.

Although there are many mysteries about the causes of the tiny variations in temperature and saltiness that set subsurface masses of water in motion, the variations can be spotted and even turned to military advantage. Early in the Second World War, while conducting antisubmarine-warfare drills off Key West and in the Caribbean, the United States Navy found that its submarine detection devices, called sonar, often failed to detect submarines known to be down below. The difficulty was traced to temperature differences in the water, which bent the sonar's sound-wave beams, as light beams are bent in a desert mirage. Temperature inversion—layers of cold water above warm—can bend sonar beams even more sharply.

Now earth satellites, using infrared wave lengths, can detect movements of warm and cold water. Temperature readings are taken by a bathythermograph, a thermometer that is lowered from a moving ship and can retain the temperature of a certain depth without responding to other water temperatures as it is pulled to the surface. To test salt content, oceanographers bring up deep-sea water in Nansen bottles, named after Norwegian polar explorer Fridtjof Nansen.

All of these instruments help track currents, which in turn help scientists acquire a better understanding of weather and climate conditions. But knowing how currents move and why they change is especially important for those who are intimately connected with the oceans—fishermen, sailors, farmers of the sea and the increasing number of workers who are engaged in drilling for oil and gas on the shelves of the world's continents.

A Cold Current Carrying Food

Even birds thrive because of the cold waters of the
northbound Humboldt Current. It is rich in plankton,
which are eaten by anchovies. In turn, the anchovies
feed larger fish as well as sea birds like the cormorants
above. The birds' droppings on nearby islands
are used by man as an organic fertilizer.

4
Waves and Tides:
What, Why, How

WIND-WHIPPED SPRAY all but hides a 114-foot lighthouse in Massachusetts Bay as it is battered by a gale's waves. Whether caused by winds or by undersea earthquakes, ocean waves can develop enormous power. Some have crashed on Scotland's shores with an impact of 6,000 pounds a square foot.

Ever since man went down to the sea in ships, the rolling waves have fascinated and awed him. The greenish-blue breakers dancing on the shore fill him with delight; the black storm crests towering over a ship's deck fill him with terror. He reels before those most destructive of all waves, the so-called tidal waves that are loosed by undersea earthquakes. He feels the rhythm of the twice-a-day waves we call tides.

Most of the waves we know best are the work of wind driving against water. The wind makes the water move up and down, but—contrary to appearance—it does not move the water forward very much. When a wave rolls over the sea, the water it disturbs is only momentarily carried forward. Each particle of water stirred up by a wave simply moves forward a bit, then down and back nearly to where it started; meanwhile the wave itself moves on to churn up other water particles. We can see how this works by watching the cork on a fishing line on a quiet day. As a wave approaches, the cork is lifted up by the wave's front slope, carried forward up to the crest, then back again as it slides down the wave's rear slope. When the wave has passed, the cork will not have moved more than an inch or so.

A wave watcher can see waves in their simplest form by tossing a pebble into a pond and watching the even succession of ripples fan out in a circle to the pond's edge. In the open sea, waves are built up in a much more irregular manner. There the wind makes wavelets of all sizes and shapes. They come together, they overtake and pass and sometimes swallow each other. If the wind is brisk, it will blow the tops off small, steep waves, forming whitecaps and heaping small waves together.

The size of waves depends on three factors: the strength of the wind, the length of time it blows and the fetch. Fetch is a seaman's term for the extent of open water across which a wind can blow. A four-mile-an-hour wind will stir up real waves, but only if there is a large expanse of open sea—a long fetch. In a sheltered harbor or cove, that same wind will create only small waves, though they will be closer together than if the wind was in the middle of the ocean. Thus, as a general rule, waves close together cannot get very

A Round Trip to Nowhere

A bobbing cork *(below)* illustrates the most important fact about wave motion: while the shape of the wave does move forward (from left to right in this sketch), each drop of water that makes up the wave remains more or less in the same place. As the crest of a wave approaches, the cork (and each drop of water) follows a circular path as it climbs up the front, reaches the peak, then glides down the rear. When the wave has passed, the cork has not moved more than an inch or two from its starting place.

big. This is a considerable comfort to those living on the coast of a narrow bay, for no matter how strong the wind may be, it cannot stir up waves more than a few feet high.

It is on the open sea, where the wind may blow over a fetch of thousands of miles, that the biggest waves have been recorded. The sailor's rule of thumb says that the height of the wave in feet will usually be no more than half the wind's speed in miles per hour. In an 80-mile-an-hour hurricane, by this rule, the waves may run about 40 feet high. But individual waves may be far higher. Whipped together by a storm, traveling at different speeds, several waves may combine to form a superwave that can rise out of the driving, howling sea to flood the biggest ship.

Most stories of big waves are taller than the waves they tell about. But the wave reported in the *Proceedings of the United States Naval Institute* is generally conceded by oceanographers to have topped all others. On February 7, 1933, the United States Navy tanker *Ramapo*, en route from Manila to San Diego, ran into "a disturbance that ... permitted an unobstructed fetch of thousands of miles." To lessen the danger from the stormy seas, the *Ramapo* ran directly ahead of the wind. Soon after midnight the executive officer, Lieutenant Commander R. P. Whitemarsh, saw by moonlight a great sea rising astern "at a level above the mainmast crow's-nest." The *Ramapo* was then on an even keel with her stern in the trough of the sea. From these circumstances and the known dimensions of the ship, Whitemarsh made a simple mathematical calculation that gave the height of the wave: 112 feet.

Despite occasional huge waves, it is the everyday sloshing of the surf that does the sea's main job of shaping the coastline. In the course of a single year, unceasing surf wears down and then rebuilds thousands of beaches, alternately removing and replacing sand in a never-ending cycle. People living on the California coast between Santa Barbara and Los Angeles have seen the surf move great quantities of sand miles along the shore in a few years, robbing some towns of prized beaches and choking the harbors of others with tons of unwanted sand.

The great power that surf has to move sand, together with the many ways in which

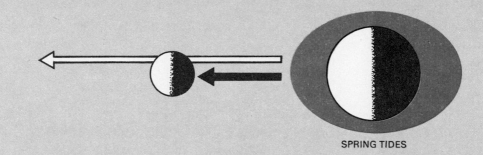

SPRING TIDES

The Pull of Moon and Sun

Tides—the twice-a-day rising and falling of ocean levels—are caused by the gravitational attraction of the moon and the sun. When these two bodies are in line (as in the new moon phase above), their pulling forces *(arrows)* add together to produce higher, or spring, tides. The moon, when it is full, is in a direct line, too, but on the other side of the earth. When the sun and the moon are at right angles, their pulls work in different directions, resulting in less movement of the seas and lower, or neap, tides.

NEAP TIDES

waves and coastal landscape may act together, accounts for the waves' ability to reshape coastlines. Each time a wave passes through shallow water, it lifts loose grains of sand from the bottom. Because the water has been stirred up by the wave, the sand grains are shifted about and settle in slightly different places from before. Such movement of countless millions of sand grains is forever changing the shape and position of beaches.

Along some coasts the shoreline is straight, the underwater slope is uniform and waves often come in directly at the shore instead of at an angle. In such places the surf simply moves sand back and forth from the beach to the underwater slope. During the summer months, fair-weather waves transfer sand from the slope to the beach, laying down a nearly horizontal layer of sand, called the berm, and building the beach outward toward the sea. On some beaches berm can be deposited at fantastic rates: 10 feet in a day, several hundred feet in a season. But it is all temporary. Once autumn storms begin, the sand will be carried back out to sea to the underwater slope, where it will be deposited in the form of winter sand bars.

Of all the waves that wash the world's shores, the twice-daily tides, which rock the oceans in response to the tug of the moon and sun, might seem insignificant at first sight. But the tides unlike the winds, which only roil up the sea's top layers, move the whole ocean. As a matter of fact, they move the earth and air, too. Every time there is a 10-foot tide in the water, the continents rise about six inches and the blanket of air that surrounds the globe bulges out toward the moon and sun to a distance of many miles.

People used to say that the tides represented the breathing of the earth. Now we know that they are caused by the gravitational pull of two neighbors in space, the moon and sun. The moon's pull on the oceans is, of course, much weaker than the earth's own, partly because the moon is smaller than the earth but mostly because it is so far away. Still, this is enough to set all the oceans rocking as the moon swings on its daily journey around the earth. A bulge of water rises on the side of the earth facing the moon. An equal bulge forms at the same time on the opposite side.

The sun, despite its huge size, is so far away that its effect on the tides is about half that of the moon. Nevertheless, the sun alternately adds to and subtracts from the moon's pull, according to the position of the sun. When moon, sun and earth are directly in line—as at the new and full moons—the moon's and the sun's pulls are added together, and we have the unusually high tides called spring tides. When moon, sun and earth are at right angles to each other—as in the moon's first and third quarters—the moon's and the sun's pulls partly cancel each other out, and we have the unusually low tides called neap tides.

But this is not the whole story of tides.
(Text continued on page 61)

These contrasting views of the same area result from a 13-foot tide tha

creates a lagoon at high tide *(above)*, a muddy flat at low tide *(below)*.

HIGH-TIDE ZONE

PERIWINKLES

MID-TIDE ZONE

MUSSELS

LITTORAL

GOLDEN STAR TUNICATES

Because the oceans do not cover the whole globe evenly but are broken up into many differently shaped basins of varying depths, the water in each basin will slosh back and forth in different ways in respones to the pull of the sun and moon. Tides in the centers of some tidal basins may be slight, and islands in such locations, like Nantucket and Tahiti, generally have tides of little more than a foot.

Tides near the outer rims of particular tidal basins, especially in funnel-shaped bays, where the incoming water has no place to go but up, are apt to be very high indeed. The Bay of Fundy, located between the Canadian provinces of New Brunswick and Nova Scotia, has all these peculiarities, compelling incoming waters to crowd into a constantly decreasing space. Here the tides reach fantastic proportions, surging up more than 40 feet twice a day and sending a four-foot wall of water—the famous Bay of Fundy tidal bore—foaming up narrow, riverlike arms of the bay. All told, each tide carries more than 3,680 billion cubic feet of water into the bay, an amount equal to all the water consumed by all Americans during three months.

When rising tides coincide with storms, they can cause frightful damage. In 1900, during a hurricane in the Gulf of Mexico, a tide rose 15 feet at Galveston, Texas, topped the sea wall and drowned nearly 6,000 people. But the most destructive of all waves are caused neither by wind nor the tug of moon and sun, but by giant disturbances under the sea. These waves have long been called tidal

Life Ruled by the Tides

A rocky seashore (*opposite*) supports marine life of many kinds, each at a depth suited to its needs. In the high-tide zone, which is under water for short periods, are periwinkles, barnacles, brown seaweed and other plants and animals that can live in air for a long time. The mid-tide zone—under water 45 to 85 per cent of the time—teems with mussels, snails, bivalve mollusks and knotted wrack, a seaweed. The bottom, or littoral, generally under water, supports golden star tunicates, seaweed and other life.

waves, much to the annoyance of scientists, who point out that the waves have nothing to do with the tides. Now scientists are encouraging people to use the Japanese name for these waves, "tsunami," which means large waves in harbors.

Tsunamis are generally caused by large earthquakes beneath the sea, but can occur after volcanic eruptions or even underwater avalanches of rock. They cross the ocean in the form of low waves at speeds up to 600 miles per hour. Individual waves, which can be as much as 100 miles long, follow each other at intervals of anywhere from 15 minutes to two hours, and the first one is not necessarily the worst. When they approach shallow water, their speed slows, but they rise as much as 100 feet and hit with unimaginable force.

Disastrous tsunamis almost always strike on Pacific shores, especially those of Japan. In 1896 a tsunami's 100-foot-high waves crashed onto the Japanese coast, taking the lives of 27,122 people. Thirteen years earlier, similar waves had wrecked village after village in Java and Sumatra and killed 36,380 people after the explosion of the island of Krakatoa. The upheaval created a series of tsunamis, and the waves went around the world, leaving their mark on tide-measuring instruments in the English Channel.

Such appalling loss of life is probably a thing of the past. A 1946 tsunami that did some $25 million worth of property damage in Hawaii and killed 150 people convinced scientists that such destruction should no longer occur. Consequently, in 1948, the United States put into operation what has become an international, Pacific-wide warning system with headquarters in Honolulu.

Now a network of seismological stations detects earthquakes, including the large ones that can produce tsunamis. If the system's tide-measuring stations near an earthquake register tsunami-wave movement, Honolulu issues a warning and transmits to each tide station through the entire Pacific area the estimated arrival time of the first wave.

In this way, tsunamis now can be anticipated and, with the help of satellites, communication is swift. Thus, it looks as though man has learned to live with—and through—these devastations of the deep.

From Stones into Sand

Rocks, deposited by glaciers 15,000 years ago, form a Long Island beach. The rocks, ceaselessly pounded by waves, are ground down by two main forces: that of water against stone, and that of stone against stone in the tumbling of the surf. Eventually, these two forces will turn this stony pile into a soft, fine sand.

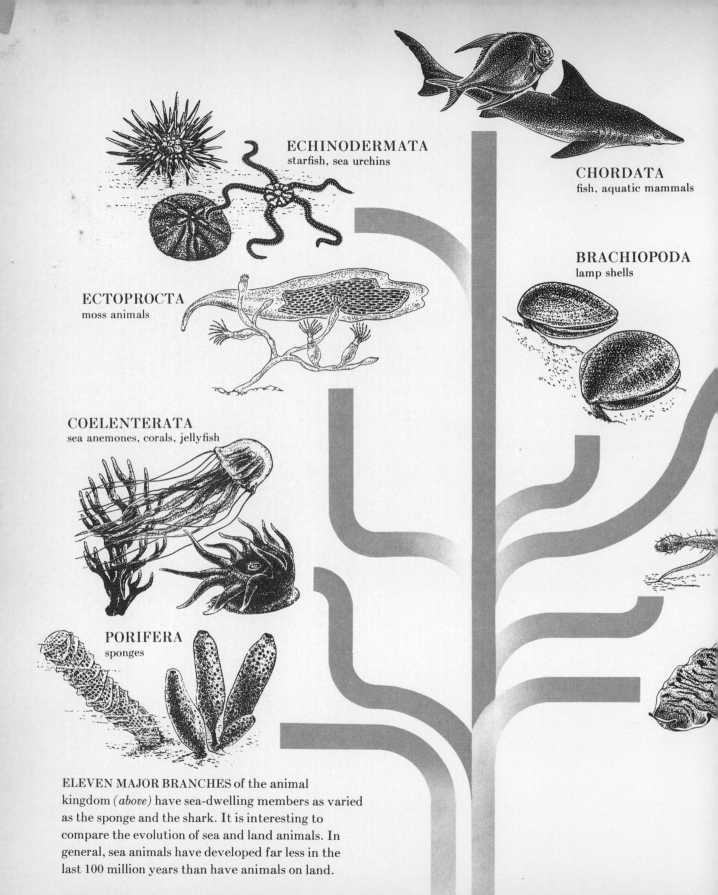

ECHINODERMATA
starfish, sea urchins

CHORDATA
fish, aquatic mammals

BRACHIOPODA
lamp shells

ECTOPROCTA
moss animals

COELENTERATA
sea anemones, corals, jellyfish

PORIFERA
sponges

ELEVEN MAJOR BRANCHES of the animal
kingdom (*above*) have sea-dwelling members as varied
as the sponge and the shark. It is interesting to
compare the evolution of sea and land animals. In
general, sea animals have developed far less in the
last 100 million years than have animals on land.

MOLLUSCA
clams, snails, octopods

ARTHROPODA
crabs, shrimps, barnacles

ANNELIDA
segmented worms

ASCHELMINTHES
roundworms, rotifers

PLATYHELMINTHES
flatworms

5

The Great Pyramid of Marine Life

In its abundance, its variety, its oddity, its beauty, life in the sea is rich almost beyond imagining. The sea's inhabitants range from the trillions upon trillions of creatures so small they cannot be seen by the naked eye to the 100-foot-long, 150-ton Antarctic blue whales, three times larger than any dinosaur. They include some of the loveliest forms that nature has ever created—wonder-

A KEY TO CHARACTERISTICS

On the following 19 pages, the animal groupings, or phyla, charted on pages 64 and 65 are examined. In addition to illustrations of members of each phylum, there are a diagram and explanation of the phylum's distinguishing characteristics. The glossary below defines some of the terms used in the captions:

SEGMENTED BODY: A body made of distinct units, or segments, joined together.

RADIAL SYMMETRY: Having similar parts that radiate, or spread, from a central point.

SKELETON: Hardened framework of a body serving as support (internal) or support and protection (external).

DORSAL: Back, or top side.

VENTRAL: Front, or under side.

GUT: Passageway into which food enters, in which it is digested and from which wastes are given off.

BODY CAVITY: Space between the body wall and internal organs.

GULLET: The part of the gut near the mouth.

ful fish that are all silver, animals that bloom like flowers while rooted to the ocean floor, glowing corals that spread in gorgeous terraced steps along tropical coasts. There are also worms that grow 90 feet long, fish and shrimp that feed off tiny animals attached to larger fish, even fish that can change to any of eight different colors.

The sea is a good place for life. It is also a great place for leftover life—jellyfish, corals, sponges, starfish, horseshoe crabs and other ancient forms that still flourish although they reached the limits of their progress long ago. As a place to live, the sea surpasses the land in several important ways—less changeable temperatures, more support against gravity's pull and, of course, more water than anywhere else on earth.

Two main facts govern the way sea creatures live: the unbelievable number of marine life forms and the utter ruthlessness with which the larger creatures eat the smaller ones. It was once estimated, for instance, that if all the eggs laid by codfish were hatched and grew to maturity, the Atlantic would be packed solid with codfish within six years. But nature does not let this happen. Only a tiny fraction of codfish eggs ever become full-sized cod, and the same can

PLATYHELMINTHES

CHARACTERISTICS: (1) Flattened body; (2) gut with single opening; (3) no body cavity. Flatworms, both those that live independently and those that live as parasites on the outside or inside of other animals, make up this phylum. Although Platyhelminthes such as tapeworms may reach 60 feet in length, most, such as the *Dugesia tigrina*, are under half an inch. Members of this phylum live in salt and fresh water and on land.

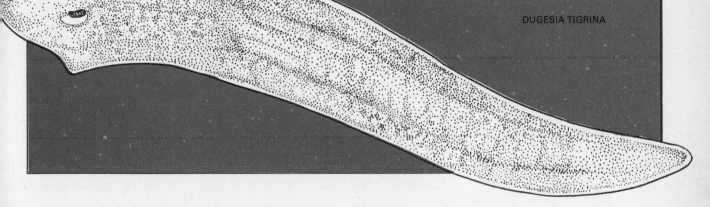

DUGESIA TIGRINA

be said for other fish. Only one sea creature in about 10 million escapes a violent death. Most of the rest meet their end inside another creature.

The community of life in the sea can be compared to a pyramid. At the base are the trillions of plants and animals so small that they can be seen only through a microscope. These support a smaller number of slightly larger living things, which feed on them; and these, in turn, are food for a still smaller number of yet larger creatures. Finally, at the top of the pyramid are the relatively few large fish and other big sea creatures that

could not exist without all the other layers in the pyramid.

A single example, given by N. J. Berrill in his book *You and the Universe*, reveals just how many lives and deaths are involved in the process of feeding just one humpbacked whale. This sea mammal "needs a ton of herring in its stomach to feel full—as many as five thousand individual fish. Each herring, in turn, may well have six or seven thousand small crustaceans in its own stomach, each of which contains as many as one hundred and thirty thousand diatoms. In other words, some four hundred billion yellow-green diatoms sustain a single medium-

PORIFERA

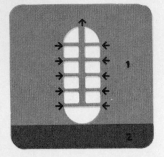

CHARACTERISTICS: (1) Body structure is filled with openings through which flows water that contains life-sustaining food particles and oxygen; (2) stationary as adults. Sponges, which make up the Porifera phylum, are the most primitive of all many-celled animals, having neither true tissues nor organs. Sponges vary in sizes from a quarter inch to six feet and in shape from the vaselike tufted sponge to the bushlike sponge called dead men's fingers.

sized whale for a few hours at the most.

It is now known that there is life even in the deepest and darkest corners of the sea. All life in the ocean can be divided into three basic types: the floaters, the bottom dwellers and the swimmers. For the most part, the floaters are found in the sunlit surface waters, although some species of floaters can sink to surprising depths. The bottom dwellers are most frequently found in shallow waters close to the shore, where worms, shellfish and innumerable other burrowing or crawling forms swarm. The swimmers inhabit many regions of the sea, particularly the upper layers.

The best place to begin examining life in

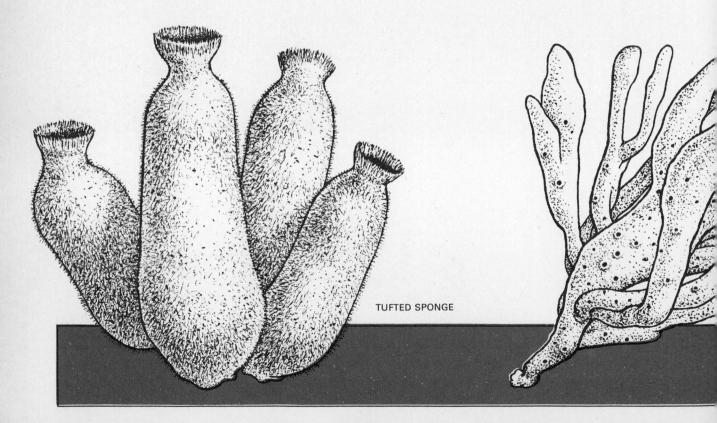

TUFTED SPONGE

the sea is in the surface waters, where there are great numbers of microscopic plants and animals that make up the broad base of the pyramid of life. At sea, as on land, the animal kingdom depends on the plant kingdom for food.

Plants alone capture the energy of sunlight and use it in making the sugar and starch that animals avail themselves of. Although large visible plants, the seaweeds of the shores, play their part in supplying food, it is a relatively insignificant role; in fact, more than 99 per cent of all plant life in the sea consists not of what most of us would recognize as plants, but of microscopic particles floating in the upper 100 feet or so of the ocean, where they can get light and energy from the rays of the sun. Although these tiny particles cannot be seen with the naked eye, they are there in uncountable numbers, suspended in the water like the motes of dust that we can sometimes see floating in a shaft of sunlight.

These living specks that are too small and too weak to do anything except drift on the currents are called phyloplankton. The most important of these specks are the single-celled algae known as diatoms. Each diatom is enclosed in a clear case that looks like the world's smallest pillbox. When looked at under a microscope, one droplet of sea water

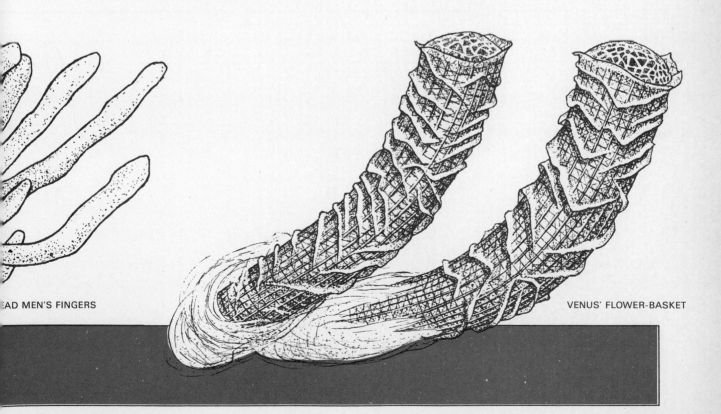

EAD MEN'S FINGERS

VENUS' FLOWER-BASKET

69

COELENTERATA

CHARACTERISTICS: (1) Radial symmetry; (2) tentacles with stinging cells; (3) gut with one opening; (4) no body cavity. Jellyfish and sea anemones (*right*), corals and the Portuguese man-of-war are all members of this phylum. Most coelenterates live in salt water, and range from seven feet to less than an inch. Coelenterates such as the jellyfish are free-floating, while others, like the sea anemone, are stationary as adults.

WHITE SEA JELLYFISH

SEA ANEMONE

turns into a dazzling show of diatoms shaped like tiny flashing bracelets, pendants, needles and anchors. Each creature builds its case from the minerals in the sea around it.

Just as land plants depend on minerals in the soil for their growth, these tiny sea plants depend on minerals in the sea. In regions where there are definite seasons of the year, the oceans, having been deeply stirred by winter storms, bring to the surface in the spring a supply of bottom water enriched with the nutritious minerals. These nutrients, together with the increasing hours of sunlight, permit the diatoms to reproduce with astonishing speed. In as little as two days they may double their numbers and spread a living carpet over great areas of the ocean. Hundreds of square miles will be tinged yellow or brown or green, as the sea takes on the hues of the tiny grains of color contained in each plant cell. Soon, however, the supply of minerals dwindles and the population explosion among diatoms comes to an end, but by then other marine life has eaten its fill of the tiny plants.

In the thick of this planktonic soup, there are also swarms of equally small representatives of almost every major division of the animal kingdom. In addition there are things that are neither plant nor animal but something in between. Typical plant-animals are dinoflagellates, one-celled living specks that, like animals, use tiny tails to move through the water but that, like plants, manufacture their own food. Some dinoflagellates are ca-

pable of giving off an eerie glow of light called luminescence. When the wind sends a ripple of dancing light through the water on a warm summer night, or a splashing oar and a moving boat trail a dimly glowing wake, it is dinoflagellates that give off the light. You cannot see them, but you can see the light—a chemical reaction touched off in these animals by the disturbance in the sea around them.

Wherever phyloplankton thrive, they are devoured by tiny animals called zooplankton. These generally float about in the water, too, some with the help of tiny fins. Among zooplankton are the smallest shellfish, the copepods. Probably the most numerous multicelled organisms in the world, copepods are no larger than a pinhead; still, they are a prime food source for larger creatures, from the smallest sardines to the biggest whales.

No one knows how many living creatures of all kinds drift in the plankton layers of the sea. No net has been made that is fine enough to catch the smallest creatures and yet maneuverable enough to trap the swiftest. However, a single quart of surface water may hold several million diatoms alone. Even larger plankton like krill, the two-inch-long shrimplike shellfish of the Antarctic that blue whales eat, exist in incredible numbers and support many species of whales and fish. One scientist has calculated that during the six months a young blue whale spends in Antarctic waters, it eats up to some 500 tons

71

ECHINODERMATA

CHARACTERISTICS: (1) Internal skeleton with spines often protruding through skin; (2) radial symmetry —usually with five parts; (3) gut with two openings. Familiar sea creatures such as sea stars, sea urchins and sand dollars belong to this phylum. Echinoderms are salt-water bottom dwellers; they have hundreds of small, tubular feet that not only aid them in moving, getting food and breathing, but even act as sensory organs. In size, echinoderms range from half-inch sea stars to yard-long sea cucumbers.

NORTH ATLANTIC
SEA CUCUMBER

HATPIN SEA URCHIN

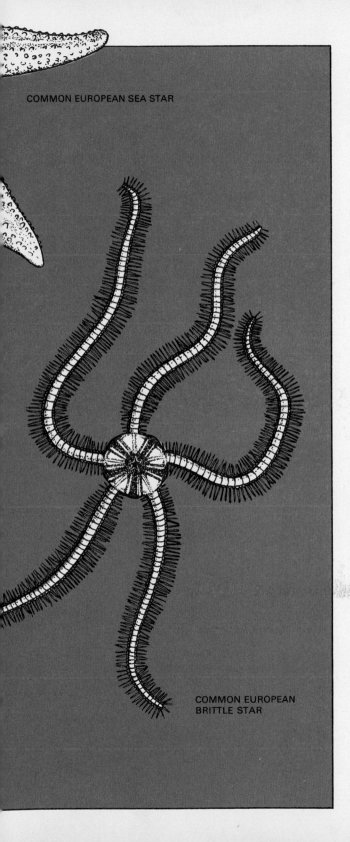

COMMON EUROPEAN SEA STAR

COMMON EUROPEAN
BRITTLE STAR

of krill. He also estimates that each year Antarctic waters spawn a billion and a half tons of krill—that is, 1,100 trillion of these planktonic creatures.

The second great zone of life in the sea is the shallow bottom along the shores. There, where sunlight can reach all the way down, the thick mass of plankton extends right to the bottom. The coastal shelf is also the one place where plants grow from the sea floor, thereby adding to the food supply for other living things.

The food supply at the bottom of these shallow seas, in fact, is so rich that all the inhabitants have to do is simply open their mouths and eat. Here the main problem is finding a place to anchor and wait for food to drop. Just how enormous a population can get was shown a few years ago when British scientists made a count of a single kind of bottom dweller, the brittle star, a cousin of the sea star. From samplings in an area off England's south coast, they calculated that there were 250 million brittle stars per square mile.

In this great world of plenty the rules are: eat, reproduce and be eaten. The lowly sea urchin is equipped with a hard, filelike structure in its mouth that is so strong that it enables the urchin to bite off pieces of rock to which algae are clinging. Other creatures have drills for boring holes through mussel shells to eat the animals inside. The scallop has 30 to 40 eyes that can see danger coming and alert the creature to move away

73

ASCHELMINTHES

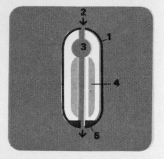

CHARACTERISTICS: (1) Body covered with tough sheath; (2) gut with two openings; (3) distinct gullet; (4) body cavity; (5) adhesive glands that enable the body to cling to solid surfaces. This is a varied phylum whose members are often wormlike. Some Aschelminthes are a foot long, but many are invisible to the naked eye. Their range is varied too; echinoderellas live in coastal waters, *Ascaris lumbricoides* in soil, and still others in fresh water.

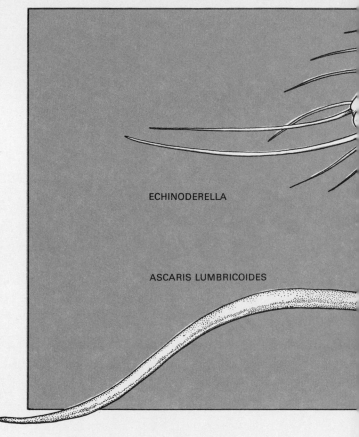

ECHINODERELLA

ASCARIS LUMBRICOIDES

to safety. The clam, however, must rely on its ability to bury itself in the mud on the bottom and then extend a long tube in search of food. If danger threatens, the clam pulls in its tube and digs deeper into the safety of the mud.

All kinds of amazing creatures, large and small, inhabit the shallow bottoms, eating the food that falls there—or eating the eaters. In sandy areas, worms burrow through the bottom, poking about in search of morsels that might have slipped down past the massed mouths above. On muddy bottoms, sea cucumbers glide along, slowly scooping the organic slime into their mouths and lick-

ing their stringy fingerlike projections, like boys eating jam.

Beyond the continental shelves, where the ocean floor falls away to greater depths, life thins out quickly. As the water beneath the surface of the sea gets deeper, the sunlight becomes less intense and the plants become fewer. In other words, the rich life of the ocean bottom ends with the limits of the continental shelves.

The third great realm of marine life is found in the wide areas of the open ocean, most of it in the upper layers. The earliest of sea creatures drifted close to the surface or crawled

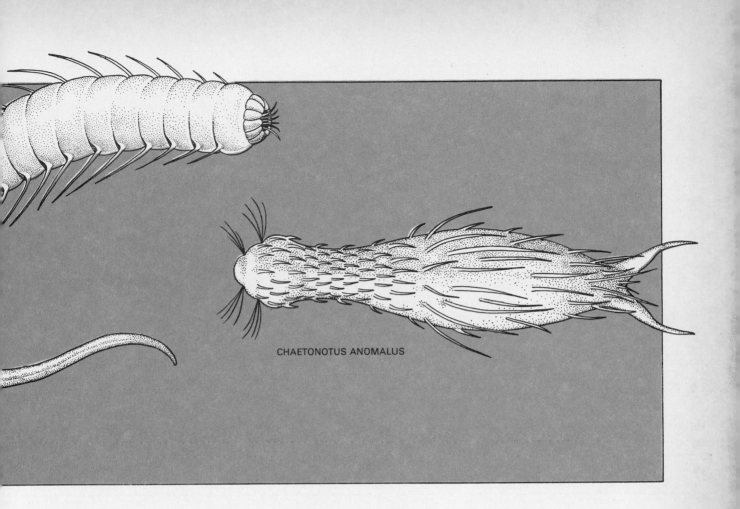

CHAETONOTUS ANOMALUS

along the bottom. The vast space in between was not and could not be occupied by the types of life that existed then. The open sea was not used until a new kind of marine animal evolved, big and strong enough to move about in the open waters regardless of the tides and currents. Today the open sea belongs to those streamlined, neckless, water-breathing, backboned animals called fish.

Fish probably evolved in the shelter of rivers and lakes and only later came down to the sea. Whales, dolphins and a few other mammals, descendants of land animals, have joined them, and marine turtles and even a few snakes also live in the ocean. But only a handful of creatures without backbones, such as the squid and the larger octopuses, live among the fish. Otherwise, the open sea belongs to the bony fish. They far outnumber their primitive fish cousins, the sharks and rays, which have skeletons of an elastic tissue called cartilage instead of bone.

Though there are more than 20,000 species of bony fish, counting both sea and fresh-water forms, they all have a similar basic design. Nearly all open-sea fish are colored to correspond with the waters they live in. Because the sea from above looks blue or green, those are the colors of their backs.

ANNELIDA

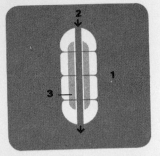

CHARACTERISTICS: (1) Segmented body; (2) gut with two openings; (3) body cavity. Leeches and earthworms are among the prominent members of this phylum, which includes animals that range in size from less than an inch to over three yards. These live in soil, all types of water and in sandy shores. The clam worm belongs to a marine class that dwells on the ocean floor. The snail leech, a member of a mostly fresh-water family, has suckers that enable it to attack other animals and feed on their blood.

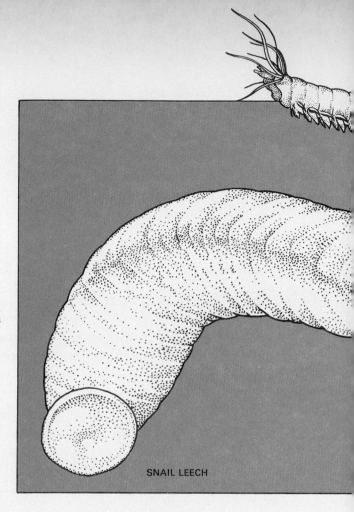

SNAIL LEECH

Because the surface waters from below look silvery or whitish, those are the colors of their undersides. This coloring usually enables fish to blend in with their surroundings and so escape being seen by their enemies.

Most open-sea fish are marked by the torpedo shape that allows them to move most efficiently through the water. Some fish are extremely fast swimmers: sailfish, for example have been clocked at 50 miles per hour, and at least for short distances marlin and tuna can move even faster. Tuna can swim steadily at a speed of nine miles per hour and are, in fact, never motionless. It has been estimated that in 15 years of life a tuna would have swum a million miles.

A few fish, like the one-ton cartwheel-shaped ocean sunfish, the stiff-bodied deep-sea boxfish and the fancier little goldfish rely on their fins to move them forward through the water. But the typical ocean fish uses its fins just for steering, steadying and stopping. Its entire body and tail, driven by one long series of muscles, flip side to side to scull it through the water; it gets extra power and speed by pumping water through its gills to help push it ahead.

A fish has highly developed organs of sense and control. Although nearly every fish possesses eyes, these are of limited use in the water's dim light and are supplemented by

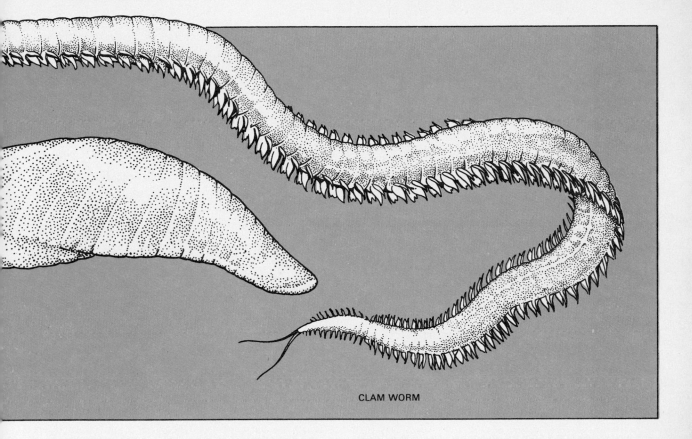

CLAM WORM

other kinds of detectors. Along each side of a fish's body there are special spots, arranged in rows called lateral lines, that are sensitive to pressure and sound. These help guide the fish by informing it of changes in the surrounding water. In addition, most fish have small organs called statocysts, inner cavities, lined with delicate hairs, that contain some loose objects like a few grains of sand. The statocysts are balancing organs that tell a fish, even in darkest waters, whether it is right side up or upside down.

Though the pull of gravity is far less bothersome to sea creatures than to land dwellers, the bones and muscles of fish are heavier than water. Therefore the fish still have to do something to keep from sinking to the sea bottom. Mackerel, tuna and some others seem to stay afloat by swimming constantly. Others, like a common mid-ocean variety, the cyclothone, have layers of lighter-than-water fat that buoy them up. Most fish, however, are kept from sinking by a swim bladder, an organ like a small balloon that is filled with gas drawn mostly from oxygen in the fish's bloodstream. But these air tanks, unlike those of a man-made submarine, cannot be quickly filled or emptied as the fish moves up or down. In this one respect, the man-made submarine is more efficient than the fish. Because of this relatively rigid swim bladder, most fish caught

BLUE CRAB

BARNACLE

at depths of more than 60 feet or so are dead when hauled to the surface: the reason is that the rapidly lessening pressure of the water on the swim bladder makes the bladder expand until it pushes against and breaks the fish's internal organs.

Although fish have no vocal organs, they are by no means silent. During World War II, ships equipped with sensitive underwater listening devices reported hearing all sorts of strange beeps, grunts and groans. At first the Navy thought the noises came from other ships. Investigators later found, to their astonishment, that marine animals were responsible, that in fact the underwater world is quite a noisy place.

Fish make sounds by grinding their teeth or by vibrating certain organs such as the swim bladder. Some of the croaks are believed to be mating calls, others seem to be warning signals passed back and forth among members of a school of fish. Commercial fishermen have tried to take advantage of these sounds by lowering listening devices over the sides of their boats in order to locate schools of fish. But most of the commercially valuable fish proved to be the most silent. Furthermore, all species have a tendency to keep quiet when they are in the vicinity of a boat.

Since fish have no eyelids and have to keep moving to stay balanced, scientists have never been able to discover much about how fish sleep. The habits of some

78

ARTHROPODA

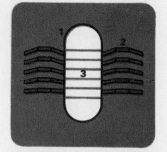

CHARACTERISTICS: (1) External skeleton formed of a hard substance known as chitin; (2) jointed legs; (3) segmented body. Arthropods account for some 80 per cent of the animals of the world. They live in the sea and air and on land. In the sea they are represented by the familiar crabs and barnacles, lobsters and shrimp; but these aquatic members of the phylum are vastly outnumbered by the land insects that make up the bulk of this grouping.

fish indicate that they do indeed sleep. The wrasse, for example, appear to bed down at night; at least they cover themselves with sand and retire. Flounders and sole often lie flat on the sea floor and could probably sleep there. Other fish can wedge themselves in the crevices of underwater rocks for the night. And there are surface swimmers that sometimes seem to rest on floating clumps of seaweed. But as for such open-sea species as the tuna, nobody seems to know if they ever really fall asleep.

Another unanswered question is whether fish age physically as they grow older. Some scientists think that when an animal stops growing it begins to deteriorate, or age. These scientists suspect that in some aqua-tic animals growth never really stops. In that case fish would not age as man does, but would slowly get bigger and bigger. However, it is impossible to test this theory at present, because the eat-and-be-eaten rule of life in the sea gives almost no fish a chance to survive to "old" age. And any fish that is not eaten apparently dies sooner or later because of disease.

It has already been noted that fish of the open sea vary surprisingly little in form from the basic streamlined torpedo shape. But for fish, as for everything else, surroundings dictate form. Thus many of the fish that do not live in the open sea but instead inhabit tropical coral reefs or sandy

ECTOPROCTA

CHARACTERISTICS: (1) Stiff outer covering, often boxlike or vaselike; (2) crown of tentacles; (3) U-shaped gut; (4) stationary. These microscopic animals are plentiful in coastal waters. The boxlike outer covering is attached to rocks, algae, pilings and to other animals. Ectoprocts have no organs to carry food, gases and wastes; instead, they use their body fluids for these purposes.

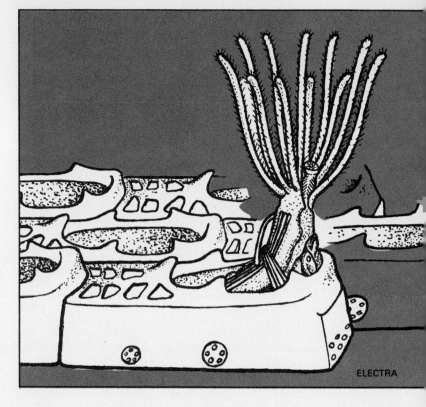

ELECTRA

shores have taken on startlingly different shapes that suit their special worlds. The sea robin has immense front fins on which it "walks" across the bottom, feeling for hidden mollusks and crabs to eat. The flounder starts life as a pancake standing on its edge, with an eye on each side and a mouth in front. But as it grows, it becomes a horizontal pancake. Its mouth twists around toward the bottom and both its eyes wind up on top. Thus it can sift the sand with its mouth as it searches out food, and simultaneously keep a sharp lookout for enemies above.

Many bottom-living fish are able to change their color and thus blend in with their surroundings. Their skins are equipped with cells that can either reveal or conceal the various bits of pigmentation, or color, to show the tone that best matches the bottom they are resting on. This is not a sign of fish intelligence, for the reaction is automatic, set off in some fish by nerves, in others by chemicals called hormones.

Although the greatest masses of marine life are found near shore and in the sunlit upper regions of the sea, there is a vast area of darkness lying beneath the water's surface that is inhabited by both animal plankton and the fish that feed on it—and on each other. These fish are quite thinly scattered through the depths because food is scarce down there, but the area they live in is so

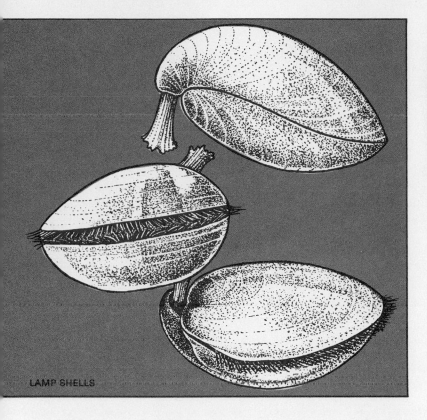

LAMP SHELLS

BRACHIOPODA

CHARACTERISTICS: (1) Double shell, with dorsal half typically larger than the ventral; (2) stalk, present in most species, attaches to a hard surface beneath the mud; (3) tentacles, used for gathering plankton. Lamp shells belong to this phylum, though they resemble many mollusks (*following page*). Brachiopods live in all the world's seas, and range in size up to three inches.

great that their total numbers are enormous.

The fish of the depths are an odd-looking collection. Unlike silvery surface fish, they are usually dark in color: red, brown or black. (Oddly enough, the scientists who explored the Mid-Ocean Rift saw brilliantly colored small fish in the perpetually black water of the undersea canyons.) Skeletons are light, tissues fragile and muscle layers thin. These fish must depend on something other than powerful swimming to find food and survive, and they have huge mouths, equipped with long needlelike teeth. Other fish have teeth that fold backward—better to catch their prey securely. One species, the viperfish, has such long teeth that they extend outside the mouth even when its lips are

closed. Other deep-water fishes, the anglerfish, have expandable stomachs, permitting them to swallow victims as large as they are.

Finding mates in the unlit depths is difficult. One species has solved the problem with a strange arrangement. The six-inch male is attached to the three-foot female, the two fish sharing one digestive system. Others make their own light—as do fireflies—and use it to recognize mates and enemies.

Fish travel in order to find food or to find a suitable place to lay eggs—which in fish is called spawning. Bluefin tuna follow a regular route each year, only part of which is now known. They spawn somewhere south

(*Text continued on page 84*)

MOLLUSCA

CHARACTERISTICS: (1) Shell made of matter containing calcium, under which is a mantle of tissue. Squid and octopuses, however, have only an internal shell remnant; (2) ventral, muscular foot; (3) gut with two openings; (4) body cavity. Clams, oysters, snails, octopuses, squids—all these animals are but a small part of this large phylum. Mollusks are found in all waters and on land. They vary in size from small snails and scallops to octopuses and 55-foot Atlantic giant squids.

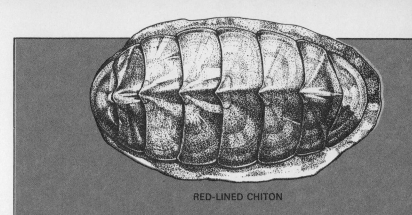

RED-LINED CHITON

MANTLE SCALLOP

ELEPHANT TUSK SHELL

LESSER OCTOPUS

of the Bahamas and arrive in the Gulf Stream in May thin and hungry, weighing about 400 pounds apiece. Eating as they swim, they reach Nova Scotia in September, by which time they weigh 700 pounds. This startling growth has been proved by catching the same fish twice, first in the Bahamas, where it is weighed and tagged with an identifying marker, then in the North Atlantic, where it is weighed again.

An even more remarkable journey is that of eels. Each fall these fish leave European rivers and head across the Atlantic to gather in a small area of the Sargasso Sea near Bermuda. There they spawn and die. When the eggs hatch, the young are caught up by the Gulf Stream and, in a journey that takes three years, float around the great North Atlantic current circling to the coast of Eu-

rope. Developing only then into young eels, they reach the mouths of European rivers just when they are ready to begin life as fresh-water creatures. And 10 years later, these fish in turn head downstream and out through the ocean to the Sargasso Sea.

It is all the more puzzling that other eels, which seem identical with the European eels, arrive off Bermuda from America to spawn, and in due course the offspring somehow find their way to American, rather than European, rivers after a mere six-month trip along the Gulf Stream. What inborn clock starts them on their journey, what inborn compass guides them, remains beyond our understanding, and the journeys of eels remain a most mysterious episode in the great drama of life and death in the sea.

CHORDATA

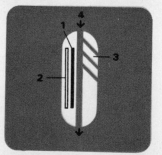

CHARACTERISTICS: (1) A flexible supporting rod, the notochord; (2) hollow, dorsal nerve tube; (3) gill slits; (4) gut with two openings. (In one group, the vertebrates, which include man, (1) and (3) are present only in unborn individuals.) The Sargassum fish (*right*) is a member of this phylum, which ranges from simple organisms to complex mammals.

6

Sharks and Other Terrors of the Sea

ROWS OF JAGGED TEETH in the mouth of a sand tiger shark give it a fearsome appearance. Though sharks use their eyes to navigate, they rely on an acute sense of smell to locate food. All sharks are meat eaters, but only some species—including, on occasions, the sand tiger—will attack man.

On a warm day in May 1959, Albert Kogler and Shirley O'Neill, both 18 and both students at San Francisco State College, decided to cool off with a swim in the Pacific. Splashing into the surf at Bakers Beach near San Francisco's Golden Gate, they swam seaward some 50 yards, Kogler in the lead. "I heard him scream," Miss O'Neill said later. "I turned around and saw this big gray thing flap up into the air. There was a threshing in the water. He screamed again. "It's a shark—get out of here!"

Looking down on the scene from the clifftop ramparts of the Presidio, the United States Army post, Master Sergeant Leo P. Day watched the struggle with the shark. "I could see the boy in the foaming red water, shouting and signaling someone to go back, go back. Then I saw the girl, swimming toward him with frantic strokes, completely ignoring his warning."

Miss O'Neill reached for Kogler's hand. "But," she recalled, "when I pulled I could see his arm was just hanging by a thread." So she put her arm about Kogler's back and started for shore. She dragged him close enough for a nearby fisherman to throw a

line and pull them both the rest of the way.

His body half drained of blood, the young man died two and a half hours later. From the teeth marks experts identified the attacker as a great white shark. For what Sergeant Day called "the greatest exhibition of courage I have ever seen," President John F. Kennedy awarded Miss O'Neill the 1961 Young American Medal for Bravery.

The full extent of the danger posed by sharks has been widely recognized only in recent decades. A World War II training book, which the United States Navy issued to men serving in shark-infested areas, said that the shark was not much of a menace to man. One national magazine portrayed the shark as cowardly—easy to scare off with a shout or a swat. Both publications were wrong; among the few human-eating sea animals—including barracuda and moray eels—sharks are the worst. The best thing is to get out of the water quietly—and quickly.

Each year sharks kill or maim several dozen human beings. In one place alone—the

waters along the eastern coast of Australia—there have been more than 200 shark attacks on humans in 150 years. Recent data reveal that each year approximately 100 attacks on humans occur in all parts of the world. Fortunately, however, less than 30 per cent of these are fatal.

Sharks are such dangerous creatures because, in fearful and amazing ways, they combine a primitive physical development with a superb adaptability. Three immense groups of muscles that run from head to tail

Death of a Man-Killer

Fatally speared, a hammerhead—one of the most notorious of the man-killing sharks—thrashes about in its death throes (*left*). Only after a long fight is this powerful fish weakened enough for the hunter to approach in safety (*above*). Found in all tropical waters, the hammerhead has a unique T-shaped head that gives it the sinister look of a prehistoric beast.

SHARK

PORPOISE

provide most of the sharks' motive power, and they have taller tails and broader fins than most fish. Their brains are tiny—seldom over three inches long even in large sharks. But they are so tough and durable that it often seems they will never die. Whalers tell of sharks that have been caught, disemboweled and thrown into the water; these gutted beasts then swam straight to whales tied alongside the ship and began tearing at the flesh.

Sharks seem to be almost insensitive to pain, but this does not mean that they lack highly developed senses. Their sense of smell is so delicate that they are nicknamed the "swimming nose"; they can detect blood or a dying fish hundreds of yards away in the water. Experts had long thought that sharks' eyesight is poor and that they do not depend on it. But when an investigator put blinders on captive sharks at the Lerner Marine Laboratory in the Bahamas, they demonstrated their reliance on the visual sense by crashing head-on again and again into walls before

learning to navigate by using their fins to feel their way.

The shark has very unusual teeth. Its mouth is literally studded with several sets of needle-sharp teeth, one row in back of another. These are loosely set in the jaw and move forward as they grow in size. New teeth replace "old" outer teeth about every six months. Shark bites have an unmistakable crescent shape and are often so deep that a major artery is severed. Many victims die from loss of blood before they can be taken to the shore.

Sharks will swallow anything: sea turtles, sea lions, birds, fish, cans, lobsters, horseshoe crabs, garbage, coal, people. One shark captured off an Australian dock had in its stomach half a ham, several legs of mutton, the hindquarters of a pig, the head and forelegs of a bulldog with a rope tied around its neck, a quantity of horseflesh, a piece of cloth and a ship's scraper. Another caught in the Adriatic, had an even stranger bellyful: three overcoats, a nylon raincoat and an automobile license plate.

SWORDFISH   MANTA

Not all of the 250 or so species of sharks are equally dangerous to man. Some are only a foot long. Others, like the dogfish, common in East Coast waters of the United States, have never been known to bother swimmers. Two—the basking shark and the whale shark—are harmless although they reach a length of 30 to 50 feet and are the largest creatures in the sea except for whales. These two giant sharks are plankton feeders, lacking the teeth needed to attack man.

The true killers, experts consider, belong to a dozen species ranging in size from five to 25 feet. Much the most dangerous of these is the great white shark, a fast-moving, powerfully muscled brute that sometimes weighs nearly four tons. Great white sharks, according to one English writer, display "a vast greediness after human flesh." They have attacked American bathers as far north as Massachusetts along the Atlantic Coast.

Another fierce variety, the hammerhead, has a weird T-shaped head that looks like a hammer, apparently helpful as a kind of

A Sign of Danger

A dark, triangular fin slicing through water has traditionally meant the presence of a shark. Less hazardous sea creatures, though, also jut parts of their bodies (*dark-colored areas*) into the air when they swim close to the surface. The porpoise exposes a portion of its back along with its fin. The swordfish shows both fin and tail. The manta, which gives the appearance of two sharks swimming side by side, is actually exposing parallel wing tips.

91

rudder for rapid turning. As many as 10 shark attacks each year in United States waters can be blamed on hammerheads. They are bottom feeders that lurk close to shore and along coral reefs, where they are a constant danger to skin divers.

The largest group of man-killers has the fitting name of requiem sharks. By far the most common of the group is the tiger shark, a striped species feared equally in the West Indies and Australia. Also common is the lemon shark, a smaller scavenger with a yellowish belly containing a digestive fluid supposed to be so powerful that, when dropped on a man's hand, it can burn the skin. No one has yet tested this bit of folklore, but it is probably no more true than the mistaken idea that a shark must roll over on its side in order to bite.

Sharks occur in nearly all climates; there is even an Arctic species, the Greenland shark. However, the vast majority of sharks are found in temperate and tropical seas, and nearly all shark attacks on humans have taken place when the water temperature has been over 70° F. Some people think that shark attacks take place when temperatures are high because it is only when water is warm that people go swimming. However, recent studies indicate there is more to it than this: shark appetites seem to go up and down with the water temperature.

Sharks have been known to swim considerable distances up rivers in search of prey. They have attacked Indian pilgrims in the Ganges many miles from the ocean, and sharks have bitten men, women and children in an Iranian river 90 miles from the sea. In one of the attacks in Iran, a British driver had driven his ambulance into the water to wash it. He was standing in only a foot of water when struck and he nearly lost a leg.

No one fully understands what makes one shark rip into a man, another circle uncertainly and another turn indifferently away. After more than 100 undersea shark encounters, Jacques-Yves Cousteau, author of *The Silent World* and expert on undersea life, has come to two conclusions: "The better acquainted we become with sharks, the less we know them; and one can never tell what a shark is going to do."

The most effective device yet found for protecting swimmers in shark-infested areas is what Australians call "meshing." Loosely hanging nets are set in place overnight in the water around the bathing beaches. These nets entangle sharks, which are then killed, thus reducing the number of sharks in the area. The nets were first tried at the big beaches near Sydney in 1937, and in just over a year they caught 1,500 sharks, 900 of them probably man-eaters. Since then the catch has dropped to 200 a year, and the number of attacks on bathers at meshed beaches has been all but eliminated.

Aside from the shark, the most dangerous salt-water fish is probably the great barracuda. Sleek, cigar-shaped, four to six feet long, this species is more feared than the

A Sword and A Bludgeon

Two well-equipped marine predators, the swordfish and the sawfish, use their specialized snouts as weapons. The swordfish hunts by plowing through a school of fish, killing, maiming and impaling its victims with its long nose. The sawfish uses a snout edged with sharp teeth to club and slash its prey to death.

SWORDFISH

SAWFISH

shark by many Florida and West Indian divers for two reasons: in the first place, barracuda outnumber sharks in those warm, reef-studded waters; in addition, even when they do not attack a swimmer, barracuda have the unnerving habit of inquisitively following him around. Barracuda have sharp eyesight and they are attracted by bright, flashing objects, by legs dangling from rafts, even by waders along the beach. When a barracuda strikes, it leaves a clean, straight-line wound that is utterly unlike the ragged tear left by a shark. Only 30 or so recorded attacks can be charged to the great barracuda. But there have probably been other attacks by these ravenous fish that for one reason or another have not been recorded. In general, however, the attack of a barracuda is much less likely to be fatal than that of a shark because the barracuda does not press its attack.

Moray eels, the fierce-looking, thickset creatures of tropical reefs, are dangerous to man in only one respect. A diver who pokes a hand into a hole occupied by a moray eel may get bitten. Furthermore the eels are very strong and they will not let go; a man grabbed by a moray may drown before he can pry himself loose. But the eel's grasp is purely defensive, and is seldom a serious menace to man.

Of the mammals of the sea, two are known to be real killers. Luckily man rarely runs into either of them.

One potential man-eater is the 30-foot killer whale. This fierce beast ranges in all seas, particularly in the higher latitudes, hunting in packs of a few up to 40 individuals, devouring penguins, fish, walruses and seals.

The other menacing marine mammal is the sea leopard, a 12-foot-long Antarctic seal that preys on smaller seals. But it also hunts other warm-blooded animals, and a sea leopard nearly caught a member of the Shackleton Antarctic Expedition of 1914-1915. First the seal lumbered across the ice after him, then dived into the water and swam under the ice, following the man by the shadow he cast on the ice. Finally it burst out again on the frozen surface in front of the man as he ran for his life. The man was saved only when another member of the party heard him yelling, ran up and shot the sea leopard.

A Community with One Body

The Portuguese man-of-war consists of hundreds of individual animals joined together for cooperative living. Divided into four specialized groups, one type makes up the saillike float; another forms the tentacles with their deadly sting; a third type digests food; the fourth is the reproduction center.

7

The Mammals That Dwell in the Sea

A SURFACING WHALE may look like an enormous fish, but it is actually a warm-blooded mammal that must breathe air frequently to stay alive. Like many whale species, the gray whale (*left*) was nearly exterminated by whalers by the 1930s. Now protected, its numbers have climbed from 100 to over 10,000.

A seagoing cow sounds like a foolish idea, yet there is an animal called a sea cow that lives in the water and is a closer relation to the grazing cow than it is to any fish. And the sea cow is just one of many mammals that have returned to the oceans, from which their most remote ancestors crawled hundreds of millions of years before.

One group of these mammals of the sea, the whales, have found the oceans so friendly that in the last 50 million years they have grown not only into the largest mammals but also into the largest animals ever to live on our planet. They are even bigger than the giant dinosaurs that once roamed the earth. Another kind of seagoing mammal, the seal, has become the most numerous group of large meat-eating mammals on earth.

From these facts it would be easy to conclude that the mammals of the ocean are doing very well nowadays. Unfortunately this is not so. At least it has not been so for the last 150 years. For another and even mightier mammal, man, has been giving the mammals of the sea a very bad time.

There is a simple reason for this. Marine, or ocean-living, mammals have the misfortune to be swimming storehouses of products man wants: fur, oil, meat. Even so, they might not be so badly hurt by man if they did not, like man, reproduce so slowly. Every year man takes about 70 million tons of fish from the oceans without seriously depleting this valuable source of food. The same cannot be said for the slow-breeding mammals of the sea, many of which have been all but stamped out to serve man's needs and desires.

The sea otter, for example, is a handsome creature with one of the world's most valuable skins. At the beginning of this century the sea otter's luxurious dark fur brought prices of $1,700 a skin; to gain this rich prize, men hunted the animal, which had been widespread along North America's Pacific Coast, until it almost disappeared. Laws now protect sea otters, and as a result, they are making a comeback and are found again in many parts of their former habitat.

Of all the mammals that now live in the sea, sea otters remain closest in form to the mammals of the land. Sea otters are the only ocean mammals that still have true hind legs. These are short, with webbed toes, and they are specialized for swimming but they are not flippers.

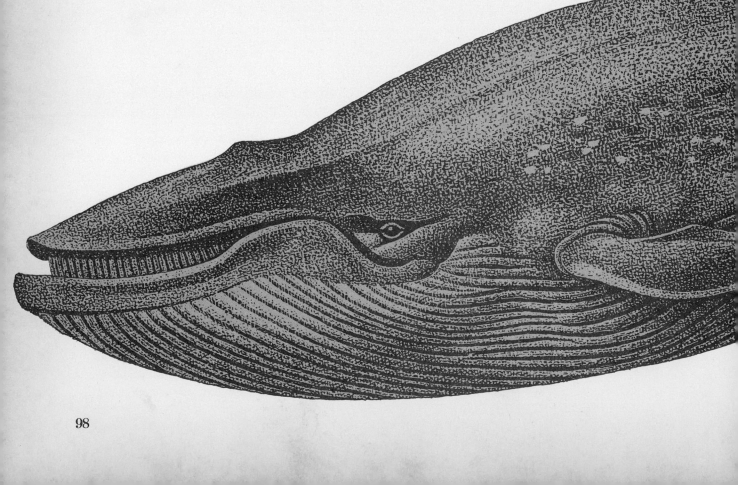

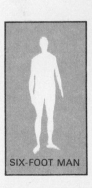

SIX-FOOT MAN

The World's Largest Animal

Sixteen times longer than the six-foot man drawn to scale in the box above and some 1,700 times as heavy, the blue whale is the largest animal that has ever existed. Though it is mature at the age of four or five, it grows for about 12 years before reaching full size. An average blue whale's carcass supplies 120 barrels of oil plus many tons of valuable meat.

HUMPBACK WHALE

SPERM WHALE

Sea cows, on the other hand, are much more obviously built for life in the ocean. These 6-to-10-foot, almost hairless creatures have flippers instead of forelegs and have lost their hind legs altogether. Their place in the mammalian world is puzzling, but naturalists think they may be distantly related to elephants. They form another group that has suffered heavily at the hands of man. Some 150 years ago, the heaviest species of sea cow—the 30-foot, three-and-a-half-ton Steller's sea cow that lived in the Bering Sea, off Alaska—was wiped out by whalers, who hunted it down for its flesh. Now only two kinds of sea cow survive: the dugong of the Indian Ocean and the manatee of tropical American and African waters.

Manatees are plant eaters and lounge sluggishly in the water of river mouths and along coasts, where their food grows. They breed

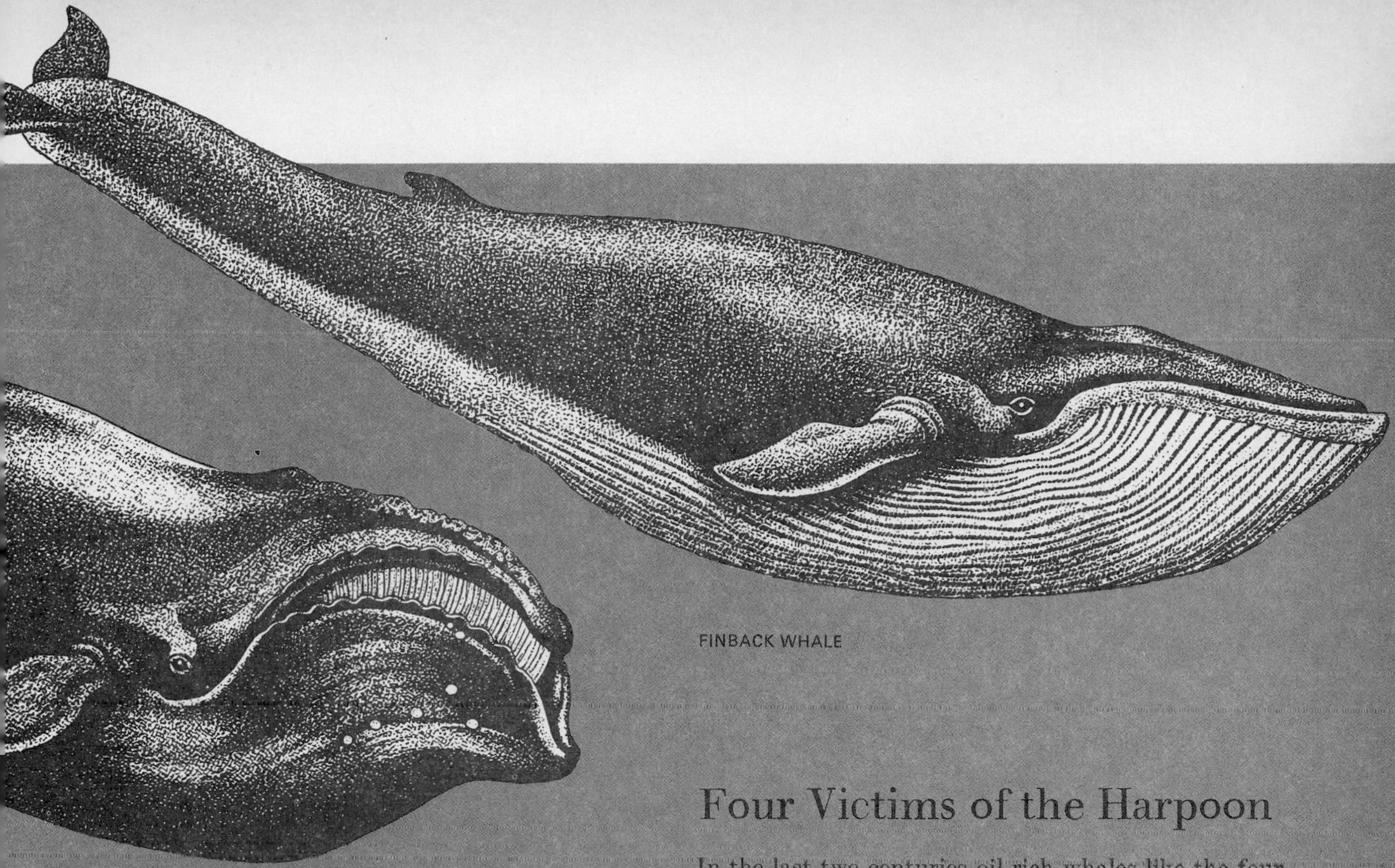

FINBACK WHALE

RIGHT WHALE

Four Victims of the Harpoon

In the last two centuries oil-rich whales like the four shown here have been relentlessly hunted by man. During the 19th century, whale oil was burned in lamps; today whale's oil is still prized as a lubricant for precision instruments. The oil, flesh and bones of whales are used to make a variety of products, from human and animal food to vitamins and cosmetics.

and bear their young at sea, and are very awkward and almost helpless out of water. Female manatees may be responsible for many of the reports of mermaids, those legendary creatures, half fish, half woman. To superstitious sailors viewing manatees at a distance, they resembled mermaids. Up close, however, there can be no confusion, for manatees are homely animals—bald, hare-lipped, mustached and thick-necked. In fact,

it is a fair assumption that only a male sea cow would find any beauty whatsoever in the female of the species.

What is believed to be the largest surviving group of big meat-eating mammals in the world today consists of about 25 million fin-footed animals of 31 species divided into three groups—the eared seals, the true seals and the walruses. Eared seals, which include sea lions and fur seals, still have visible ears;

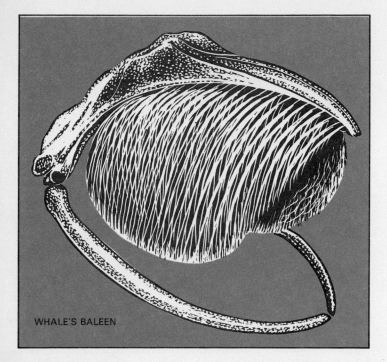

WHALE'S BALEEN

A Built-in Food Strainer

Most large whales eat only very tiny ocean animals and plants called plankton. To catch this food, the whales have a feathery strainer called a baleen inside their mouths (*left*). As a whale swims into a mass of plankton, (*right*) water rushes into its mouth, the plankton snags on the baleen, and the water squirts out the sides of the mouth. When a mouthful of food has built up on the baleen, the whale licks it off with its enormous tongue.

the true seals and walruses have lost these projections, which hamper swift underwater swimming, and in general have moved closer to the streamlined fish shape.

Fur seals were butchered in the north for 200 years. In the Pribilof Islands off Alaska, their numbers were reduced from more than two million to scarcely more than a hundred thousand by the early years of the 20th Century. Since 1911 the United States has administered an international agreement to protect the Pribilof herds. The effect on the seals has been startling; their numbers are now back to about two million.

Sea lions were never hunted with such savagery, largely because they have no great commercial value. One variety is the so-called trained seal, often seen at circuses or in zoos. Even without training, it likes to toss and catch fish as it frolics off its native Pacific rocks.

True seals range more widely than the eared varieties. One of them, the monk seal, lives in the tropics, a sharp break from the preference of most seals for cold water. The largest true seals are the sea elephants, which grow as big as 16 feet long and 12 feet around and have an odd 15-inch "trunk" hanging down over their noses. Almost exterminated for their blubber, sea elephants are making a comeback in the Antarctic and on Guadalupe Island off Lower California.

A sadder story is that of the walrus. Like its smaller cousin the fur seal, the 3,000-pound walrus was once plentiful throughout the Arctic regions. But hunters pursued it relentlessly because, in addition to its hide and oil, its two-foot tusks commanded a high

price in the ivory market. The cruelest of the hunters' tactics was to catch a walrus calf and beat it until it cried. Since walruses are devoted parents, every adult within hearing would rush to the calf's aid—and into the hunters' trap. Now the few walruses left roam remote areas of Greenland and the Arctic.

Of all the mammals that have taken to the sea, none has made the change more completely than the whale—and none has been more savagely hunted by man. From early times men have been awed by these mighty giants of the deep. Even now, when modern men and their machines have driven most of the big whales to a last Antarctic stronghold, it is impossible for most of us to look upon these wonderful animals without being aware of their power and grandeur.

Not all whales are big, of course; some are no more than four-and-a-half feet long. Of the 100-odd species, almost half are the relatively small dolphins and porpoises. There are two basic kinds of whales, into which all species fall: the baleen whales and toothed whales. Baleen whales, which are the biggest of all, have huge strainers of a tough and flexible stuff called whalebone, or baleen, inside their mouths. The whales with teeth include the broad-domed, 60-foot-long sperm whale, the killer whale—actually a dolphin —and all the other dolphins and porpoises.

The whale is so completely adapted to life in the sea that many people still think of it as a fish. It is easy to see why because, while it is warm-blooded and breathes air, the whale certainly looks like a fish and in many

(*Text continued on page 107*)

Huge bull walruses wallow in the ocean off Alaska. Now found only in

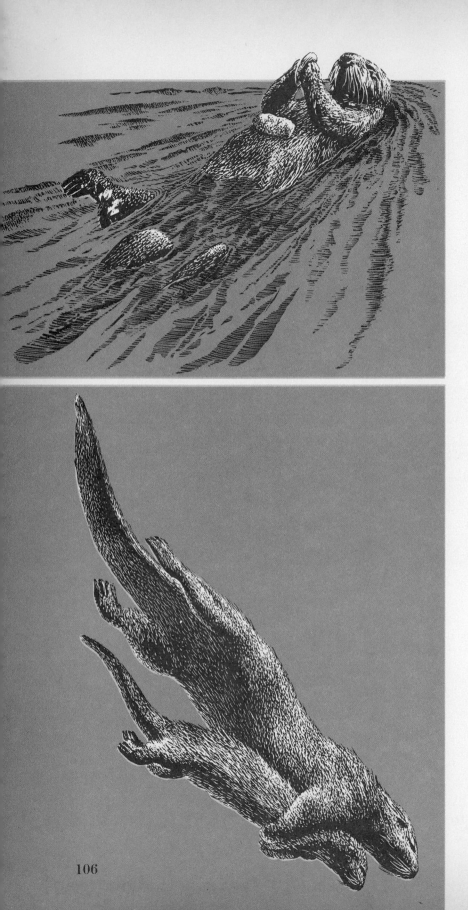

An Ocean Otter

A sea otter, one of the most playful of all
ocean mammals, swims along on its
back while it eats a shellfish. It opens the
mollusk by cracking the shell against a
stone that it has placed on its chest *(left)*.
Mother otters usually hold their babies to
protect them, as shown at left below.
But sometimes, when mothers go off to
hunt for food, they tether their young
close to shore with a long piece of seaweed.

ways it lives like a fish. It has no need, as some other sea mammals do, to go on land to bear its young. It is marvelously streamlined. Its neck bones have shortened so that the head merges with the trunk. Its forelegs have become fins and its hind legs have completely disappeared.

The only remains of the whale's external ear are openings on either side of the head no thicker than a pencil. Their nostrils have moved from the front to the very top of the head and have become one or two blowholes that enable the whale to breathe without raising itself more than a few inches above the water's surface. A thick layer of blubber, or fat, not only helps keep it warm in cold polar seas but also acts as a food reserve when the whale travels to warmer waters where the kind of food it likes may not be so abundant.

The biggest whales are bigger than any land animal could be. The largest one ever caught was a female blue whale that measured 113.5 feet and probably weighed 170 tons, as much as 2,267 average men.

A whale can grow to such size because water holds up its weight evenly over its body, thus avoiding the concentrated forces at points of support that land animals must withstand. The whale's great size provides room for the muscles that give the whale swimming power. The entire rear third of a whale is an engine of enormous muscles. These enable the whale's 12-foot tail to move in a semicircular motion that works like a

ship's propeller, building up as much as 520 horsepower in a 90-footer, according to the estimate of one scientist. Large blue whales can travel at 20 knots when necessary, and can run all day ahead of a whaling ship traveling at 10 knots.

All big whales except the sperm whale are baleen whales. They feed on small creatures of the sea by swimming along at slow speed with their mouths open. Their jaws are so wide that a tremendous amount of water pours in and is then forced out at the sides through the baleen strainers, which hang down like a curtain. Great numbers of tiny marine animals are caught in the baleen as the water passes through. Every now and then the whale's tongue wipes the baleen clean and passes the food back to its gullet.

Many whales pass about six months of the year in polar waters, where the feeding is best, and then travel to tropical seas to breed and bear young, undoubtedly so that their babies will have warm water to swim in until they grow a protective coat of blubber under their skins.

The female blue whale generally gives birth to a single calf every other year. Female blues are somewhat bigger than their mates, and their calves are astonishingly large—23 feet at birth in the case of a typical blue-whale calf, or almost a third the size of its mother. For seven months the female blue nurses its baby, supplying the calf with a ton of very rich milk a day, according to one estimate, while lying still on the surface of the sea. By the time the blue calf is ready to seek out food for itself, it is more than 50 feet long, as long as full-grown whales of many species. By the time it is two years old it may be 75 feet long.

The sperm whale, whose oil provided the wealth of New England's great 19th Century whaling industry, is in many respects the most interesting of all whales. It is the only big whale with teeth, which are like pegs about eight inches long. The teeth are all in the lower jaw, and they fit into holes in the leathery upper jaw when the long narrow mouth is snapped shut. The sperm whale needs its teeth to fight and kill its favorite food, the giant squid. It dives down more than half a mile to feed, nosing along the bottom for squid and octopus, sometimes staying there for 40 minutes before coming up to blow. Blowing, or spouting, is simply the exhalation of a whale, a great mixture of stale air and water vapor ejected into the air.

The sperm whale's name is derived from spermaceti, the oily wax found in a storage tank located in its huge square-fronted head. Spermaceti is lighter than water, and scientists formerly believed that this material helped the animal to stay afloat. Now it is thought to be connected with the whale's amazing ability to dive deep and come up relatively speedily without suffering the "bends," the agonizing pains that humans

get when they surface too rapidly from a dive.

Whales cannot breathe while underwater, naturally. But their enormous lungs help them stay submerged for astonishingly long periods of time—60 to 90 minutes. If they stay underwater too long, of course, they drown like other mammals. This fact has provided proof that sperm whales do dive deep. Every once in a while a drowned whale is found entangled in a transoceanic cable. A cable-repair ship once found a dead whale caught in a cable at a depth of 3,720 feet.

The sperm whale's appetite for giant squid is the source of one of the ocean's most valuable products. The whale swallows squid whole, but has never been able to digest the hard parrotlike beaks of its prey. These some-

The Gentle Dugong

Sea-dwelling mammals, like the dugongs, have specialized forms that have evolved as they adapted to life in the water. The dugong, for instance, has flippers instead of forelegs. Its outer ears have disappeared to give it a more streamlined shape, and even its heavy bones help it stay under water.

The Streamlined Dolphin

The white-sided dolphin shown here has a body shape so well suited to life in the water that in many ways it looks like a fish. Dolphins communicate with each other by a wide variety of calls and noises. They are very friendly and playful animals that often frolic around the bow of a passing ship.

Special Skeletons for the Sea

The skeletons of a dolphin (*below*) and of a sea lion (*below, right*) show some similarities to the bones of land mammals, but also some changes suited to life in the water. Most mammals, for instance, have five "finger" bones. These are present in the sea lion's front limbs, but only four remain in the dolphin. Like land mammals, the sea lion still has its hind legs. But the dolphin has lost them entirely. Instead, the dolphin has an extra-thick backbone that gives it added swimming strength.

times fail to pass through the digestive tract, causing the gradual formation of a dark, sticky material called ambergris. It smells foul at first, but after processing becomes a substance that is famous for making perfumes hold their scent. Recently, substitute products have tended to take the place of ambergris in perfumes, and some countries now prohibit the use of whale products. But top-grade ambergris is still valued. Whales often vomit up their ambergris, in which case it may be found floating in the water or washed up on a beach. It is also found when a captured whale is cut up.

No one has yet figured out an intelligence test for whales. But smaller sea mammals, the dolphins, have been studied in captivity,

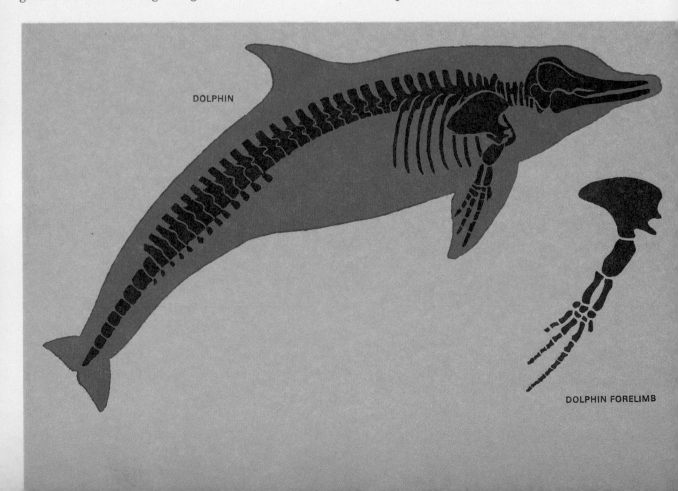

DOLPHIN

DOLPHIN FORELIMB

and have shown considerable ability to learn. Both dolphins and whales are social animals, with a tender regard for their young and a readiness to go to the aid of a fellow in distress. When a dolphin is injured, for example, other dolphins gather around and try to push the wounded member of their school up to the surface so that it can breathe.

Dolphins make many different sounds, but mostly they whistle and chirp when they talk to each other. Clicking sounds help them navigate and find food, for they have a system that works like sonar, the underwater detection device; using their own "sonar," dolphins can trace the echoes that bounce off food, for example, and locate their meals.

Whales also have ways of using sound to communicate with each other, to navigate and to locate masses of tiny marine organisms. But the whale has not been able to cope with its one great enemy, man. In the past two and a half centuries, man has slaughtered one species of whale after another.

The first species brought near to extinction was the Atlantic right whale. Whalers of the 17th Century called this black, oil-rich 60-footer a "right" whale because it floated when killed; most other whales were "wrong" because they sank when killed and so were lost. The Atlantic right whale was almost gone by the end of the 17th Century, whereupon whalers next gave chase to the bowhead, also known as the Greenland or Arctic

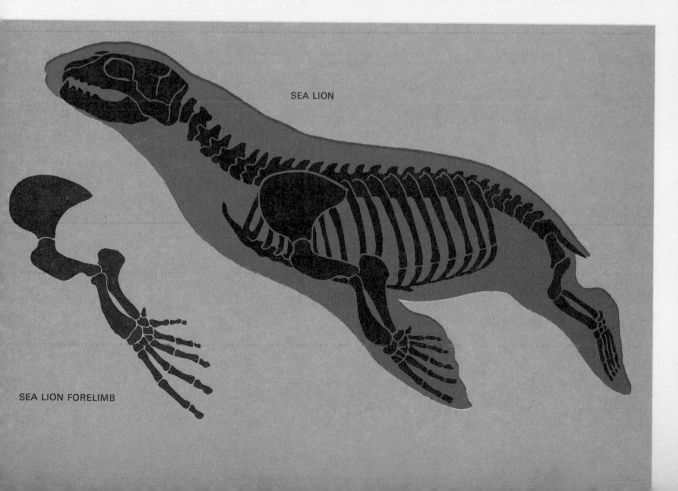

SEA LION

SEA LION FORELIMB

right whale, whose baleen alone could bring $10,000 in world markets. For in those days fashionable women wore corsets of whalebone. Bowheads were soon all but wiped out.

In the last year of the U.S. Civil War a Norwegian whaler invented a gun for firing grenade-carrying harpoons. Soon other Norwegians developed power-driven catcher boats and devices for pumping air into captured whales to prevent them from sinking. These refinements revolutionized the whaling industry, making it possible for whalers to go after the big whales—the blue, the finback, the humpback—that had been "wrong" for earlier mariners. In the Antarctic, operators of giant whaling-factory ships have killed more than one million whales in the past 50 years. The efficient slaughterers of the 20th Century possibly have killed five times as many whales as all the famous whaling fleets of the 19th Century.

Because of the number of whales being killed—in one season almost 30,000 blue whales alone were caught—several nations agreed in the 1930s to limit their yearly catch. However, whale populations contin-ued to decline. Not only the blue whale but many others were headed for extinction.

In 1946 the newly formed International Whaling Commission sharply limited annual catches and banned altogether the killing of gray, right and bowhead whales. Since 1966 the same prohibition has protected blue and humpback whales. And in 1976, the IWC added the finback to their list, except for allowing a few hundred to be caught each year in the North Atlantic.

Estimated populations for these endangered whales show that the bowhead is still in danger of becoming extinct. It is possible, though, that it can survive with continued protection. The most encouraging sign that protection does its job is the healthy increase in the number of blue whales. By the mid-1960s, there were only a few thousand left. Roaming as they do between Antarctic and equatorial waters, these magnificent mammals were a prize catch for whalers in the Southern Hemisphere. Now there are 10,000 or more making their annual long-distance journeys. Clearly, international agreements have helped the survival chances of the most gigantic creature ever to live on earth.

Highly Intelligent Mammals

Four dolphins seem to grin as they wait for a handout of fish at Marineland in California. Dolphins have complicated brains comparable to man's, making them responsive to training They delight visitors with a variety of stunts like jumping through hoops and playing games of basketball.

8
Man and the Future of the Sea

The seas are mankind's last frontier on this planet. For ages, man treated the great waters as little more than hunting grounds for fishermen and highways for ships. Now he is awakening to the fact that beneath the waves lies a vast territory every bit as challenging as outer space—and much more promising in terms of reward.

For centuries salt has been extracted from sea water by evaporation. Sand, gravel and shell are dredged up from the bottom for use in construction. And ingenious techniques have been conceived to derive energy from the movements of the sea. For example, a hydroelectric dam near the mouth of the Rance River in northern France successfully uses the rising and falling of tides to generate electric power.

Someday, it may become possible to turn the up-and-down motion of the waves effi-

ASTRIDE SCAFFOLDING, a Southeast Asian fisherman adjusts his nets. The seas have long been a means of food and travel, but man has only recently begun to use this part of his planet more effectively. New ways are being found to extract food, mine undersea minerals and quickly cross the vast oceans.

ciently into electrical energy. Someday, too, energy may be created by devices that exploit the difference in temperature between surface and deep tropic waters.

The sea can also be turned to the benefit of agriculture on the land. In Israel, for instance, sea water is desalted by heat to provide fresh water for extensive irrigation projects. And in the future, tugboats may haul icebergs to warm, dry regions such as Saudi Arabia, where they could serve as a source of irrigation water.

One of the most basic and beneficial ways to use the ocean is to farm it, much as we farm the land. This is called aquaculture, or mariculture, and it includes the rearing of both plants and animals under controlled conditions. A great deal of experimentation and commercial production is presently being done, especially in Asian countries like Japan where there is little land for agriculture. The Japanese have raised oysters commercially for a thousand years or more. Other fish being raised either at commercial or experimental farms include salmon, clams, shrimp, lobster, squid and abalone.

Seaweed has become another aquaculture item. It is used in many parts of the world for food, fodder and fertilizer. It is also used in industry as a thickener and gelling agent.

Although there are thoughts of farming fish in the deep sea, aquaculture will probably

Harvesting the Ocean Crops

Fishing with methods ranging from primitive to sophisticated, man annually catches some 40 million tons of fish. Australian aborigines fish much as their ancestors did, with spears from canoes (*above*). In contrast, an American fleet in the Atlantic (*left*) uses electronic gear to locate schools of fish. Man's next step in harvesting the seas may be aquaculture —the controlled planting and raising of fish.

117

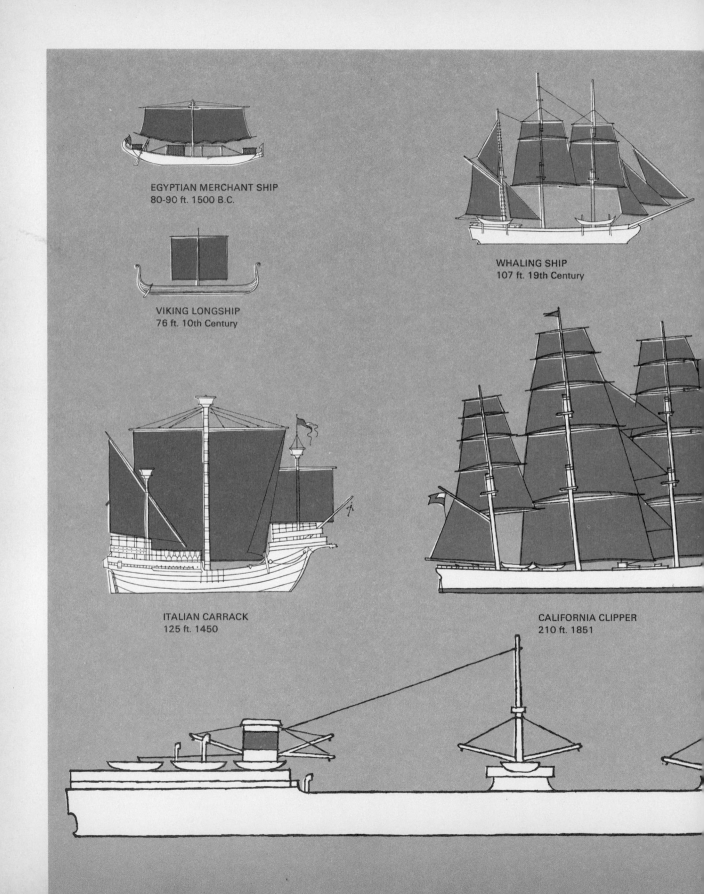

EGYPTIAN MERCHANT SHIP
80-90 ft. 1500 B.C.

VIKING LONGSHIP
76 ft. 10th Century

WHALING SHIP
107 ft. 19th Century

ITALIAN CARRACK
125 ft. 1450

CALIFORNIA CLIPPER
210 ft. 1851

Progress on the Seas

In his long struggle to master the sea, man has launched an enormous variety of ships. His first major advance after the crude prehistoric dugout was craft propelled by oars or a sail, such as the Egyptian merchant ship and the Viking longship (*far left*). Pushed by a need to explore and aided by improved technology, man began building larger ships with many sails. This age was typified by far-ranging vessels like the Italian carrack, and the whaling and clipper ships of the 19th Century. The present-day era of steam power began after 1807, the year Robert Fulton built the steam-driven *Clermont*. Now, steel ships like the whale factory—over two football fields long—are not unusual.

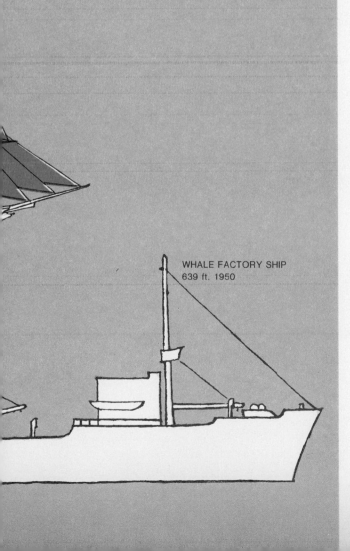

WHALE FACTORY SHIP
639 ft. 1950

remain mostly limited to the shallow waters of the continental shelves. In time, these waters may supply a significant portion of the world's protein—more than 100 million tons, according to some estimates. But for the immediate future, the most visible and important activity there involves the search for oil and gas. Already, offshore oil wells provide some 20 per cent of the world's oil requirements and about 10 per cent of its natural gas requirements.

The first offshore petroleum operation was launched almost a hundred years ago, in 1896, when a company in California merely extended an onshore field and drilled from wooden piers. For many years, offshore wells were drilled only in shallow waters from rigid platforms whose supports rested on the sea floor. But, in the autumn of 1947, an undersea well was drilled in the Gulf of Mexico from a mobile platform composed of two World War II Navy barges and a tank-landing craft. Following this breakthrough, a variety of floating platforms were designed for drilling operations in the deeper waters of the Gulf of Mexico and off the Venezuelan coast. The technical skills gained there have helped many nations of the world in discovering oil beneath their territorial waters.

The best places to look for oil offshore are areas where the sediment is at least 3,000 feet thick. Basins of sediment like this seem to be concentrated along the continental shelves. But geologists have been finding still thicker deposits of sediment under the slopes leading to the deep plains and also

119

under the rises at the margins of the abyssal plain. Consequently some drilling is being done at these greater depths, though the cost is far higher and the added distance from shore brings extra problems.

As though there were not enough oil on land in the Middle East, over half the off-shore oil found to date is in the Persian Gulf. A shallow basin, the Gulf is the site of the second largest oil field in the world, estimated to have a total production potential of over 25 billion barrels.

Geologists were not surprised when they discovered the resources of the Persian Gulf, since the onshore fields of Saudi Arabia and Iran lay so close by. But they were positively amazed by their findings in the North Sea. This area has become an entirely new oil region, and a very exciting one. Until the mid-1960s, the North Sea, which is part of the continental margins of the lands surrounding it, was best known for its foul weather. Although there were small oil fields in Britain, the Netherlands and Germany, almost no one considered the North Sea to be a potential spot for oil until a huge gas field was discovered under farmland in the Netherlands, at Groningen. Its geological formation was so similar to another formation in Yorkshire, England, that geologists decided to investigate undersea terrain between the two land areas.

Today, in spite of such hazards to exploration as waves that reach more than 90 feet high and winds that reach 125 miles per hour, a number of giant oil and gas fields

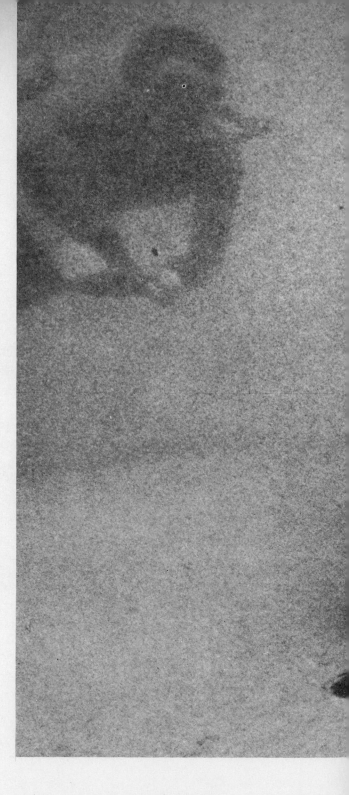

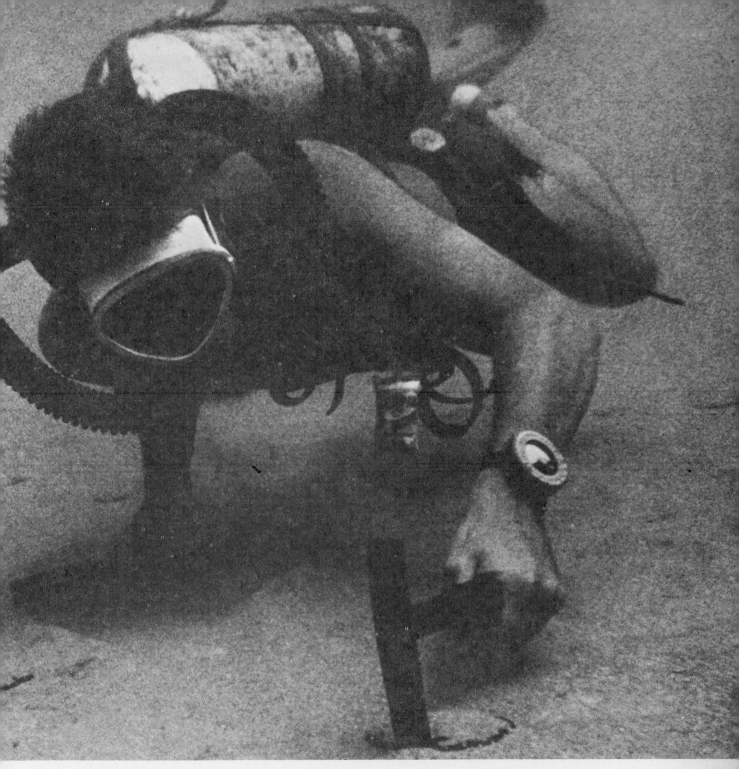

A New Underwater Freedom

A skin diver, probing for evidence of underwater oil deposits, wears a portable air supply on his back. Once, man could stay underwater only as long as his breath held out; modern equipment has given him a new mobility.

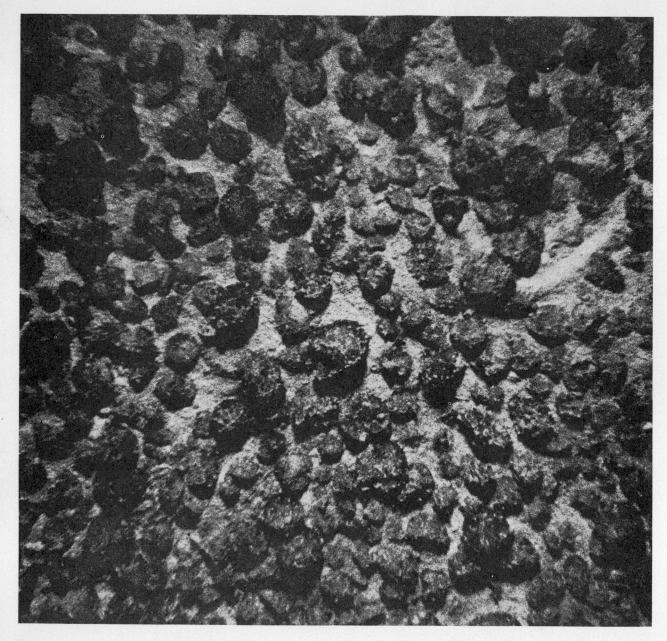

Mining the Ocean's Floor

Manganese nodules are found on the ocean
floor in deep water. They are valuable sources of
nickel, copper and cobalt as well as manganese.
Many governments and private companies have
spent considerable sums of money to explore and
develop methods for mining the nodules.

have been located in the North Sea, primarily in British and Norwegian waters. Thus far, more than 15 billion barrels are known to exist. The first major British field, known as the Forties, is estimated to contain almost two billion barrels; the first major Norwegian field, Ekofisk, apparently holds approximately one billion barrels.

The success in drilling these oil wells and erecting production platforms has required a wholly new measure of fortitude and ingenuity on the part of everyone involved. The mobile drilling rigs used for exploration had to be designed with especially strong structures and 16.5-ton anchors for North Sea conditions. When the oil was located, enormous fixed platforms were constructed for full-scale production. These extra-heavy steel structures, which are topped by drilling derricks, weigh some 62,700 tons. In order for them to withstand the force of the North Sea's immense waves, each of the four platform legs is pinned to the sea floor with 11 steel tubes; the tubes are four feet in diameter and can be driven as much as 250 feet through layers of sand and clay in order to reach a firm bottom of rock.

Four such platforms have been installed in the Forties field about three miles apart. Clusters like this will increasingly dot the seas, and the experience gained from building and maintaining them will be put to good use when other difficult areas are brought into production.

Although the hunters of offshore oil are correctly concentrating on the continental margins, scientists are now predicting that deep-sea trenches may also hold deposits of oil. Trenches are created when an oceanic plate of the lithosphere dips below a continental plate. Island arcs are formed on the continental side of the trench by volcanic action when low-density crystal rock begins to melt as it dives into the hot asthenosphere. Great quantities of sediment and organic matter then accumulate near the islands and the continent, and scientists reason that the earth's heat at these spots helps turn decaying organic matter into oil.

But oil and gas are not the only resources there. Metals are thought to be extracted from the dipping plate as it begins to melt in the earth's interior. They are then returned to the surface as molten rock rises into layers of sedimentary rock, which are in turn squeezed up into mountains near a trench. This process explains why the Andes, formed by such squeezing, hold untold quantities of metals.

The ocean bottom between ridges and trenches is another highly promising source of minerals, and numerous governments and private companies are determined to exploit this resource. The minerals are scattered about in the form of nodules that often look like black potatoes.

These nodules contain different mixtures of about 20 metals, the composition depending on the area and the ocean the nodules are found in. Iron and manganese are the predominant ingredients, but nickel, copper and cobalt are also generally present. The nodules are produced when dissolved minerals in the sea begin to collect around a nonmetal nucleus—a bit of coral, basalt, clay, or even a shark's tooth. Although some of the details of this process are not yet clear, it occurs on an enormous scale.

The Pacific Ocean has been singled out as the richest source of the deposits: 1.5 trillion tons of the nodules are estimated to be there. By 1980, or perhaps even sooner, nodule mining may begin in the mid-Pacific. There are three methods for the continuous recovery of nodules. One of these systems uses compressed air that is pumped into a long pipe at various levels. The pipe connects the mother ship with a dredging device on the ocean floor. The compressed air injected into the pipe lowers the density of the water inside it, and the difference in pressure pulls in water from the outside, vacuuming up the nodules.

A similar, but less complicated, method of recovering nodules is a hydraulic system. Nodule-bearing water is forced up a pipe to the mother ship by a powerful pump.

The third basic method is quite different. It is called the "continuous line bucket system" and it uses a long, braided plastic cable to which are attached dredge buckets at intervals from 80 to 165 feet. The cable, which is kept in rotation by machinery on the mother ship, must be long enough to drag along the ocean bottom. As it does so, each bucket picks up about one to five tons of nodules. When a bucket arrives at the ship, it dumps its nodules, continues across the ship and descends again.

Oil, gas, minerals, food, energy—these are but a few of the treasures that are locked away in the ocean. Man has begun his assault on the sea, and he is certain to continue the effort. But sometime in the future the sea itself must come to an end. Astronomers predict that the sun will pass through a "red giant" stage before turning into a cold, dark lump of matter drifting through space. This will not happen for at least 3,000 million years—perhaps not for 10,000 million years. But when the sun does turn into a red giant, it will swell up to nearly 100 times its present size, emitting enormous quantities of heat in the process. In the red light of the sun the earth's temperature will rise, causing life to shrivel, and then the seas will finally boil away in clouds of steam.

A Taste of Tomorrow Today

When the U.S. Navy submarine 571—the *Nautilus*—first slid into the water in 1955, it signaled the start of a new era in man's relation to the sea. The *Nautilus* was the world's first atomic-powered vessel. Nuclear energy has increased the range and speed of specially designed ships—and has made the seas seem smaller.

Index

Numerals in italics indicate a photograph
or painting of the subject listed.

Credits

The sources for the illustrations that appear in this book are shown below. Credits for the pictures from left to right are separated by commas, from top to bottom by dashes.

Cover—Flip Schulke from Black Star.
Table of Contents—Leslie Martin—Jim Egleson—Otto van Eersel—Matt Greene—Leslie Martin—Kenneth Gosner of the Newark Museum—Rudolf Freund—James Alexander
6, 7—Fritz Goro
8, 9—Ward's Natural Science Establishment, Leslie Martin
10, 11—Andreas Feininger, Rudolf Freund
13—Matt Greene (2), Nino Carbé
14, 15—Anthony Petrocelli
16, 17—Leslie Martin, René Martin
18, 19—Rudolf Freund
20, 21—Rudolf Freund
23—Official U.S. Navy Photo
24—Conrad Limbaugh
26, 27—Jim Egleson

29 through 37—Kenneth Fagg
39—Jim Egleson
41—Courtesy Dr. N. L. Kenkevitch
42, 43—Werner Wolff
44 to 48—Otto van Eersel
51—Dr. Robert C. Murphy
52—Edward Rowe Snow
54 through 56—Matt Greene
58, 59—Michael Rougier
60—drawing by Jack J. Kunz, Dr. Douglas P. Wilson (2)—M. A. Wilson
63—Eliot Elisofon
64, 65—Kenneth Gosner of the Newark Museum
67—Otto van Eersel—Ben Goode
68, 69—Otto van Eersel—Leslie Martin (3)
70, 71—Otto van Eersel—Leslie Martin

72, 73—Otto van Eersel, Leslie Martin (4)
74, 75—Otto van Eersel, Ben Goode (3)
76, 77—Otto van Eersel, Ben Goode (2)
78, 79—Jack J. Kunz (2), Otto van Eersel
80—Otto van Eersel, Leslie Martin
81—Leslie Martin, Otto van Eersel
82, 83—Otto van Eersel, Leslie Martin (2), Matt Greene—Leslie Martin
84, 85—Otto van Eersel, Fritz Goro
86—Russ Kinne
88, 89—Peter Stackpole
90, 91—Kenneth Gosner of the Newark Museum
93—Kenneth Gosner of the

Newark Museum
95—Kenneth Gosner of the Newark Museum
96—Peter Stackpole
98, 99—Rudolf Freund, Virginia Wells
100, 101—Rudolf Freund
102, 103—Kenneth Gosner of the Newark Museum
104, 105—Fritz Goro
106—Jack Schoenharr
108, 109—Guy Tudor
110, 111—Kenneth Gosner of the Newark Museum
113—Peter Stackpole
114, 115—Michael Rougier
116, 117—Hank Walker, upper right Fritz Goro
118, 119—James Alexander
122, 123—Matt Greene
125—Ralph Morse
Endpapers—Virginia Wells

For Further Reading

Angell, Madelina, *The Fantastic Variety of Marine Animals.* Bobbs-Merrill, 1976.
Bergaust, Erik, *Colonizing the Sea.* G. P. Putnam's Sons, 1976.
Boyer, Robert, *Story of Oceanography.* Harvey House, E. M. Hale, 1975.
Brindze, Ruth, *Sea: The Story of the Rich Underwater World.* Harcourt Brace Jovanovich, 1971.
Brown, Joseph E., *The Sea's Harvest: The Story of Aquaculture.* Dodd, Mead, 1975.
Carrighan, Sally, *The Twilight Sea: A Blue Whale's Journey.* Weybright and Talley, 1975.

Copps, Dale G., *The Savage Survivor: 300 Million Years of the Shark.* Raintree Publications Ltd., 1976.
Cousteau, Jacques, *Provinces of the Sea.* Abrams, 1975.
Darby, Ray and Patricia, *Conquering the Deep Sea Frontier.* David McKay, 1971.
Field, Adelaide, *Challenge of the Sea Floor.* Houghton Mifflin, 1970.
Foster, John, *The Sea Miners.* Hastings House, 1975.
Fraser, F. C., *British Whales, Dolphins & Porpoises.* The British Book Centre, 1976.
Howard, George, *How We Find Out about the Sea.* Transatlantic Arts, 1974.

Idyll, C. P., *Abyss: The Deep Sea & the Creatures That Live in It.* Crowell, 1971.
Limburg, Peter R., and James B. Sweeney, *Vessels for Underwater Exploration: A Pictorial History.* Crown, 1973.
Macinnis, Joe, *Underwater Man.* Dodd, Mead, 1975.
McCoy, J. J., *Sea of Troubles.* Seabury Press, 1975.
McNulty, Faith, *Whales: Their Life in the Sea.* Harper & Row, 1975.
Read, Ritchard, *The Living Sea.* Penguin Books, 1975.
Riedman, Sarah R. and Elton T., *Home is the Sea: For Whales.* Abelard-Schuman, 1971.

Scheffer, Victor, *Natural History of Marine Mammals.* Scribners, 1976.
Simon, S., *Projects in Oceanography.* Franklin Watts, 1972.
Soule, Gardner, *Remarkable Creatures of the Seas.* G. P. Putnam's Sons, 1975.
Thomes, Joann F., *et al.*, *Waters of the Earth: Investigating Oceanography.* Cambridge Books, 1976.
Viertel, Janet, *Blue Plant: The Ecology of the Oceans.* Grosset & Dunlap, 1973.
Williams, Jerome, *Oceanography.* Franklin Watts, 1972.
Wolfe, Louis, *Ships That Explore the Deep.* G. P. Putnam's Sons, 1971.

Acknowledgments

The editors are indebted to Ross Nigrelli, Director, New York Aquarium, Brooklyn, N.Y. and Xavier Le Pichon, Research Associate, Oceanography Department, Lamont Observatory, Columbia University, N.Y., who read the text and commented on their respective areas of study. The editors are also indebted to the staff of the LIFE Nature Library edition of *The Sea*, from which this volume has been adapted. The staff for this edition was Stanley Fillmore, editor; Eric Gluckman, designer; Peter Chaitin, Tony Chiu, John von Hartz, writers; Eleanor Feltser, Susan Marcus, Theo Pascal, researchers; Eleanore W. Karsten, copyreader; Virginia Wells, art assistant.